Contents

List of contributors   v

Chapter 1   Introduction   1

Chapter 2   Funding   11

Chapter 3   Waiting   21

Chapter 4   Rationing   33

Chapter 5   Primary care   43

Chapter 6   Workforce   55

Chapter 7   Quality assurance   67

Chapter 8   The private sector   81

Chapter 9   Long-term care   91

Chapter 10   Patient and public involvement   101

Chapter 11   Health inequalities   111

Endnotes   125

Contributors

John Appleby is Director of Health Systems at the King's Fund. He previously worked in the NHS and at the Universities of Birmingham and East Anglia as senior lecturer in health economics. John has published widely on many aspects of health service funding. His current work includes research into health care performance measures and rationing.

Andy Bell is Head of Public Affairs at the King's Fund. He is responsible for managing media and Parliamentary work at the King's Fund.

Anna Coote is Director of Public Health at the King's Fund, and leads work on health improvement, regeneration and tackling health inequalities. Anna was formerly Deputy Director of the Institute for Public Policy Research. She has also been adviser to the Minister for Women (1997–8) and a Senior Lecturer in Media and Communications at Goldsmiths College, London University. She is also a journalist, broadcaster and author.

Christopher Deeming is a Researcher in Health Systems at the King's Fund. Before taking up this post he worked within the NHS as an information and policy analyst; he has also led a variety of health service development projects. He works at the King's Fund in the Health Systems programme, where his main research interests include the finance and performance of the NHS.

Nancy Devlin is Fellow in Health Systems at the King's Fund. Her recent research has focused on the measurement and valuation of quality of life. Nancy previously held senior lecturer posts in economics in New Zealand. She has also published on a range of health economics topics, including health care system reforms, economic evaluation, production functions, health care spending, rationing, equity and the economics of dental care.

Steve Dewar is Acting Director of Health Care Policy at the King's Fund. He specialises in the areas of regulation and performance and accountability. He has a background in operational research, and research and development in clinical effectiveness. Steve has worked in the NHS for most of his career, typically at the intersection between health authorities, NHS Trusts and a research unit to promote the take-up of evidence into practice.

Belinda Finlayson is Research Officer at the King's Fund and leads work on recruitment and retention of NHS staff in the Health Care Policy team. She also has an interest in regulation and international issues. Belinda has a background in journalism and has worked as a health reporter in both the UK and New Zealand.

Dr Stephen Gillam is Director of Primary Care at the King's Fund and an honorary clinical senior lecturer in the Department of Primary Care and Population Sciences at Royal Free/UCLH Medical School. Steve began his career in general practice before moving into public health medicine following a period overseas with Save the Children. He worked previously as a consultant in public health medicine/medical adviser for Bedfordshire Health Authority. He continues part-time clinical practice in Luton.

Anthony Harrison is Fellow in Health Systems at the King's Fund. He worked in the Government Economic Service until 1981. Anthony has published extensively on the future of hospital care in the UK, on the private finance initiative and on waiting list management. He is currently working on a series of papers using a systems analysis approach to different parts of the health care sector.

Baljinder Heer is Research Officer in Public Health at the King's Fund. Her current work interests include inequalities in health, community safety and mental health. Previously, Baljinder held various academic posts as a nutrition scientist, social researcher and tutor. She has worked at the Institute of Brain Chemistry & Human Nutrition, Aberdeen Maternity Hospital and Newham General Hospital. She is a Registered Public Health Nutritionist.

Janice Robinson is Director of Health and Social Care at the King's Fund. She leads a team that works to improve the integration of care and support for people who have continuing health and social care needs. Janice has published widely on the care of older people, including work on long-term care funding, age discrimination in health and social care, and the care service labour market.

Ruth Tennant is Manager of the King's Fund Imagine London Programme, which aims to involve children and young people more actively in shaping a healthy capital city. Ruth worked previously at the Audit Commission as Private Secretary to the Controller, and was co-author of A Fruitful Partnership: a study of partnership working in the public and private sectors. She has also worked in the European Parliament in Brussels, specialising in European regional policy.

1 Introduction

In 1997, Labour came to power with a promise to 'save the NHS'.[1] Its manifesto pledged to cut the numbers of people waiting for care, improve the quality of hospital services, end waiting for cancer surgery, cut bureaucracy, initiate a new public health drive and raise spending on the NHS in real terms. The manifesto also promised to abolish what Margaret Thatcher described as the 'most far-reaching reforms of the National Health Service in its forty year history' – the internal market.

The Conservatives' White Paper introducing the internal market was published in 1989.[2] Five years later, in 1994, the King's Fund published a collection of papers evaluating its impact.[3] The conclusions of the evaluation were mixed; much of the direct research indicated 'little actual change of any kind and even less that could be attributed to the reforms in key areas of quality, efficiency, choice, responsiveness and equity.' But in some areas there appeared to be potential at least for real gains, for example, from giving GPs more control of local health spending.

Now, five years on from a change of government, it is time to review health policy once again. What did Labour inherit from the Conservatives? What has this Government promised? What measures have been introduced and what impact have these made on the NHS, on social care, on the nation's health?

Tracking the effects of change

Evaluating health policy is not an easy task. There are seldom unambiguous indicators of success or failure. It can be extremely difficult to attribute changes observed in some indicators to particular policies or, in fact, to any health policy. Nevertheless, it is important that policies be evaluated as far as is possible for the effects they have, or are projected to have, on people's lives.

One obvious indicator by which to judge health policy is mortality. Between 1970 and 1999, the mortality rate for all causes of death fell from 1,048 to 698 per 100,000 people (*see* Figure 1). The death rate for ischaemic heart disease has declined by 40 per cent since 1970; and for cerebrovascular disease it has more than halved (*see* Figures 2 and 3). However, these trends stretch back many years and appear to be almost completely unrelated to changes in government, let alone to changes in the resources devoted to health care, how the NHS is organised, or which health policies are given priority by any government.

Such changes in mortality are, of course, the outcome not only of the performance of the NHS (and policies designed to improve its performance) but of decades of exposure to health services. Policies to improve child health today, for example, may only come to fruition forty to sixty years later, as that generation reaches the age at which heart disease and cancer begin to cause significant numbers of early deaths. Clearly, then, the increase in the population's life expectancy over the last five years (*see* Figure 4) cannot and should not be attributed to the abolition of the internal market or any other measures introduced by this Government.

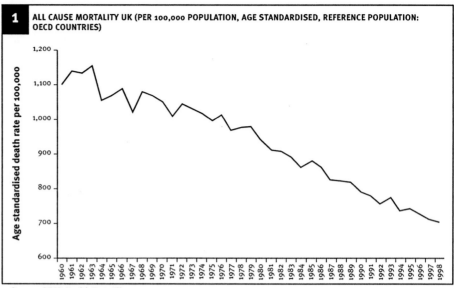

1 ALL CAUSE MORTALITY UK (PER 100,000 POPULATION, AGE STANDARDISED, REFERENCE POPULATION: OECD COUNTRIES)

Source: OECD Health Data File, 2001

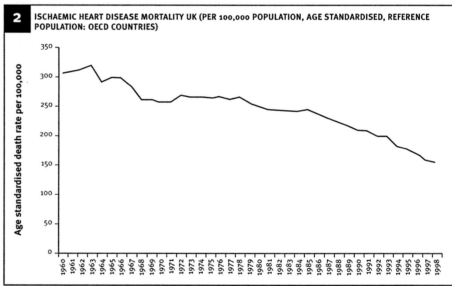

2 ISCHAEMIC HEART DISEASE MORTALITY UK (PER 100,000 POPULATION, AGE STANDARDISED, REFERENCE POPULATION: OECD COUNTRIES)

Source: OECD Health Data File, 2001

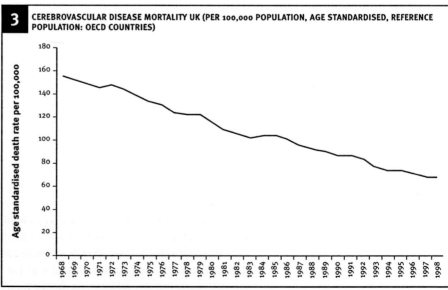

3 CEREBROVASCULAR DISEASE MORTALITY UK (PER 100,000 POPULATION, AGE STANDARDISED, REFERENCE POPULATION: OECD COUNTRIES)

Source: OECD Health Data File, 2001

Doing things right is not the same as doing the right things.

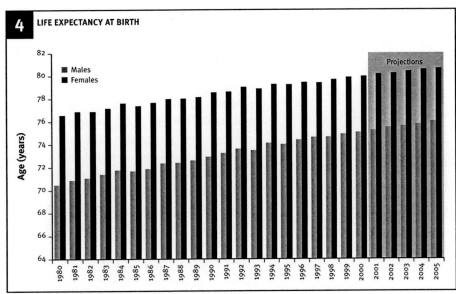

4 LIFE EXPECTANCY AT BIRTH

Source: OECD Health Data File, 2001

Moreover, health *care* is only one determinant of health. It is now well-established that measures of broad population health, such as mortality rates and life expectancy, are affected by non-health care factors – lifestyle, income, education and so on. These factors are at least partially within the remit of governments even if they are never fully under their control.

For all these reasons, any evaluation of health policy needs to take into account all areas of government action. In lieu of hard evidence on the effects of policies on people's health, it must examine what has been pledged, what actions have been taken and whether factors that were supposed to change as a result of government policies have indeed changed in the period under review.

The shape of the review

Doing things right is not the same as doing the right things. Throughout this review, therefore, we have aimed to address two broad questions that can be asked of any policy: first, was it in our judgement the *right* thing to do? And, second, what did it achieve? We focus here on the following policy areas:

- Funding
- Waiting
- Rationing
- Primary care
- Workforce
- Quality assurance
- The private sector
- Long-term care
- Patient and public involvement
- Health inequalities

The list reflects specialist work streams at the King's Fund and is obviously not comprehensive. We have not addressed mental health, for example, because the King's Fund is currently conducting a major inquiry into mental health in London and the results will not be available until early in 2003. Nor have we attempted to review the full reach of organisational change in the NHS, or specific functions such as midwifery, palliative care or dentistry, or the effects of health policy on particular

The Government's commitment to a universal, free, effective health care system available according to need and funded through taxation is beyond doubt.

groups, such as children, older people or minority ethnic communities. Some of these are subject to separate studies (recently completed or under way) and have been omitted here in order to keep the review to a manageable length.

For each policy area, the review sets out Labour's inheritance, initial promises and policies, and their elaboration and extension over the last five years. It then assesses broadly the success or otherwise of the Government's approach. We draw on as much evidence as possible in support of the critique, although some areas – such as NHS funding, waiting and health inequalities – lend themselves better to quantified analysis than others, such as quality assurance, long term care and public involvement. Our verdicts, set out at the end of each section and drawn together at the end of this introduction, provide a brief 'report card' summary of how we judge the Government's record in the period under review.

Emerging messages

We embarked on this exercise without a fixed view of what the final balance sheet might look like. The picture is complex but some clear messages emerge. The Government's commitment to a universal, free, effective health care system available according to need and funded through taxation is beyond doubt. This was made abundantly clear in *The NHS Plan* in 2000 [4] and, more recently, by the Chancellor, Gordon Brown.[5]

There is less certainty about the role of the private sector – so long beyond the pale of Labour's ambitions for the NHS. The Government is evidently shifting towards a more positive view of the contribution the private sector can make to health care. In respect of the finance of major capital projects it has already made this shift, and it appears to be preparing the ground for a substantial shift in provision, too. However, it is not yet clear whether this represents a new direction of travel or a stop-gap operation. Are we at the start of a major reconfiguration of the health care system, towards one that is publicly financed and regulated, but independently organised and delivered? Or is this a pragmatic move to lever in extra support for a growing and improving public sector organisation? It seems likely that the Government itself does not know which way to jump and is currently testing the water to see what is politically viable, rather than preparing a principled case for leading in one direction or another.

Pragmatism and principle

Since 1997, unlike the earlier period reviewed by the King's Fund, the ideological basis for Government health policy has lacked definition. Moving away from old Labour's welfare socialism and rejecting the free-market creed of the Conservatives, New Labour has not yet developed a coherent and principled set of criteria to guide its decisions. It has experimented with some ideas – the stakeholder society, communitarianism, the 'third way' – but none seems to fit comfortably or to be robust enough to support a journey through uncharted territory. To fill the void, Labour appears to be ready, on questions beyond its basic commitment to a universal service, to substitute pragmatism for principle. As the Prime Minister famously put it, 'what counts is what works.' One message from this review is that finding out what works is a long-term, costly business that seldom provides conclusive evidence. Where no one is sure what really works, and where there are no clear principles to guide policy-making, there is a danger that the process will become muddled and incoherent at best or, at worst, cynically opportunist. Public confidence is likely to be undermined, as voters fail to see why the Government is acting, where it is heading or whose interests it is serving.

The Prime Minister told the House of Commons recently that the NHS encapsulated his political philosophy.[6] The Government has clearly signalled its belief in the NHS. However, that belief is unclear in its character. The NHS is in far too profound a state of upheaval, as a result of myriad changes introduced by the Government, to provide a clear picture of what the Government stands for – unless it is 'modernisation', which cannot be passed off seriously as a political philosophy.

Unresolved tensions

There are several unresolved tensions arising out of this ill-defined ideological terrain. An obvious example is the tension between central and local control. The Government clearly wants to be seen to grapple with the NHS by asserting strong leadership and direction from the centre. An overwhelming impression to be drawn from this review is one of relentless, almost hyperactive intervention. A formidable torrent of pledges, policy documents, laws, regulations, advice and guidance has issued from the Department of Health, without let-up since 1997, to knock the system into shape: ironing out disparities, raising standards, improving productivity, increasing responsiveness, extending services, meeting unmet needs. One consequence is that the centre is held responsible for everything that goes wrong. It is therefore not surprising that, in the course of the five years, the Government has become increasingly interested in devolving responsibility – to primary care trusts and high-performing acute trusts with 'earned autonomy'. But the extent of its commitment to devolution is unclear, and the question of how to trade off local empowerment and equity between geographical areas remains unresolved. Ensuring that sufficient first-rate services are available everywhere is a fine aspiration but not practicable in the short or medium term.

A second area of tension is around the relative importance of health and health care. This Government, more than any other, has committed itself to reducing health inequalities and promoting a public health agenda. But both Secretaries of State – Frank Dobson and Alan Milburn – have established a strong identity as champions and defenders of health care, leaving health to junior ministers. Social care has likewise had second billing. The Prime Minister has chosen to stake his reputation with the electorate on sorting out the NHS, rather than, say, on reducing health inequalities or improving social services.

Media coverage of health policy, reinforcing the Government's emphasis, has focused almost exclusively on the NHS. Money has been poured into the NHS rather than into measures aimed at preventing illness or promoting independence amongst vulnerable groups that might help to check the rising tide of demand for treatment and care. An unresolved question is whether the aim of providing decent health care should be allowed to take precedence – as it undoubtedly does – over the aim of improving the chances of enjoying decent health for those who are most vulnerable to illness and premature death. One is about delivering a service, the other is about redistributing risk and opportunity. In theory, both can be given equal weight, although no government has yet shown how to do so. Shifting priorities from health care to health would require a philosophy grounded in more than a belief in the NHS.

The Government has tried to do too much, too soon, and has relied too heavily on structural change to restore a service suffering from decades of under investment.

A third area of tension is between radical and conservative tendencies. The Government wraps its policies in radical language. It speaks of saving the NHS – through 'modernisation'. But while health policy has seen numerous changes over the past five years, fundamental questions about the future of health and health care have not been fully considered.

The case for a more radical approach rests on evidence about the changing health needs of the population and the changing nature of health care. The prospect of continuing change in medical and information technology suggest that hospitals as we know them today may not be needed in 10 or 20 years time, yet the private finance initiative is locking the Government into traditional patterns of acute care for 30 years or more. The evidence also suggests that community nurses, health visitors, midwives, care workers and community development workers hold the key to health improvement at local level, especially in disadvantaged areas. But the need to extend and strengthen this section of the workforce is not reflected in the balance of investment in recruitment and training, or in the way local services are being reorganised. The Government is extremely nervous of meddling with the traditional co-ordinates of the system. 'Modernisation' is predominantly about more and better doctors and nurses, and more and better hospitals. Ultimately it may not be possible to sustain the NHS without radically altering it – but small 'c' conservatism still has the upper hand.

There are further tensions around long term care and around patient choice. Where the funding of long-term care is concerned, the Government has been unable to reconcile notions of fairness and sustainability, and has not yet come up with a plan that inspires confidence. As for patient choice, it remains unclear whether this really is to be an organising principle for the NHS and, if so, how it can be reconciled with collectivist principles such as equity and efficiency. The drivers towards consumerism in health care, as elsewhere in society, may prove to be irresistible, in which case a decision will have to be made about which of these principles should take precedence.

Achievements

Despite these tensions, there is much to commend in the Government's record to date. It has declined to flirt with alternative funding mechanisms and substantially increased levels of public finance for the NHS. It has introduced, through NICE, a new system for transparent, evidence-based rationing. The Commission for Health Improvement (CHI) is starting to establish itself as an important regulator in the NHS. National Service Frameworks are beginning to provide a new and more standardised perspective on health care. Primary care trusts now command widespread support. NHS Direct and walk-in centres are innovations that have proved popular with users. The Government's approach to two vital issues – improving the quality of health care and workforce management – has been carefully considered, comprehensive and thorough. It has managed to achieve closer integration of health and social care and better regulation of social care – both sorely needed. It has put health inequalities on the policy map and made far greater efforts to reduce them than any of its predecessors.

Failures

There have been some tactical errors, such as the early focus on cutting waiting lists instead of times, and the botched attempt to abolish Community Health Councils. The Government has tried to do too much, too soon, and has relied too heavily on structural change to restore a service suffering from decades of under investment. This has meant, for example, that primary care organisations have been overloaded with new instructions and pushed to the limits by reorganisation, so that they are unable to meet all the new expectations that have been heaped upon them. Similarly, area-based strategies to tackle the causes of ill health have suffered from project overload.

Sometimes, policies have been sound but implementation has been of poor quality or uncomfortably slow. Efforts to reduce waiting, to expand the workforce and to give primary care organisations responsibility for population health, have been hindered by a failure to anticipate the full costs of change in financial and human terms. Occasionally, the Government has been guilty of prevarication – for example, in introducing health inequalities targets. But a constant refrain throughout the review is that it is too early to expect tangible results from policies introduced less than five years ago.

There have been few outright failures of policy. The refusal to follow the recommendations of the Government's own Commission on funding long term care, has left users and carers dissatisfied and has failed to mend a rickety system. In the case of using private finance for new hospitals, the Government has entered into a massive building programme without setting out a strategy based on an assessment of our future requirements, and without transferring any substantial risk from the public to the private sector.

In spite of these weaknesses, the prospects for health and health care are more promising than suggested by the balance of media-based commentary. This is to some extent the Government's own fault. It has readily played to the gallery, instead of leading the debate, and has set itself up to be knocked down. By raising public expectations about 'saving the NHS' the Government has created hostages to fortune, endangering the reputation of the service for the longer term.

Overall, the direction of travel seems to us to be well judged and much of the detail is admirable. More credit is due than is currently paid – as the following brief summary of the review's main findings suggests.

The verdicts

Funding: The NHS has received historically significant increases in funding – well above the level of inflation since 1999. Visible evidence of the new money is still hard to find – but this should change if extra investment is maintained. The Government now seems more in step with recorded public opinion on devoting more of the nation's wealth to health care. However, fundamental questions about how much money the NHS should get and how it should be spent remain unresolved.

Waiting: Policies on waiting for NHS treatment threaten to distort clinical priorities and divert management energies. Although reducing the time people wait for health care is an important policy goal in its own right, severity of condition is not sufficiently taken into account. A more evidence-based and systematic approach to controlling waiting is required.

Rationing: The establishment of NICE is an important achievement, helping to bring transparency and evidence-based consistency to decisions about new treatments.

The impact of government targets and priorities on other areas of treatment and care raise rationing dilemmas that remain obscured and are not being addressed. Local NHS managers and doctors are compelled to make trade-offs between different patients every day, with little support or guidance and barely any reference to the public.

Primary care: Ambitious reforms of primary care have removed many of the worst features of fundholding and appear to command widespread support. But the Government is pushing an under-resourced sector to do too much too quickly. Primary care trusts need more time and resources to make the changes that are expected of them.

Workforce: The NHS remains desperately short of staff in many areas. Many of the causes of this problem date back more than five years. The Government is now making major efforts to tackle the shortages. There are early signs that it has succeeded in increasing staff numbers. It is not clear whether it can hold on to staff and offset the effects of retirement. However, a long-term vision on the future shape and roles of the NHS workforce remains to be formed. Too much of the present effort has been devoted to doctors and nurses, rather than to other equally essential health care workers.

Quality assurance: The Government has introduced radical and far-reaching reforms of the way quality is assured in UK health care. From the regulation of individual professionals to the assessment of whole organisations' performance, Labour's reforms could revolutionise the way the public judges the NHS and its workforce. However, it is still unclear how much they will affect the quality of care received by individual patients.

The private sector: The Government's enthusiasm for involving the private sector in the NHS is insufficiently grounded in evidence. It has gambled that what is built today with private finance will be fit for purpose in a decade or more. Its plans for greater private sector involvement in provision remain unclear. Is it looking to the private sector for expertise it believes the public sector lacks, or hoping private companies will provide a greater stimulus to service improvement? While the case for using spare capacity in the short term is obvious, the Government has failed to define what kind of longer-term relationships it wants to build with the private sector.

Long-term care: The Government has not succeeded in establishing a fair and sustainable system for funding long-term care. It has removed some anomalies from the system, but may well be creating new problems in their place. Integration between health and social services is improving, and both are now better regulated than before to protect users from poor quality care. Progress could still be seriously impeded by acute shortages of funds for social care.

Patient and public involvement: Emerging policies on patient and public involvement suggest a significant change in the culture of the NHS. While the impact to date has been limited, the Government's promotion of enhanced patient choice may begin to knock down the paternalism that has characterised much of the NHS to date.

Health inequalities: The Government deserves credit for putting the 'health gap' on the policy map, but it has allowed it to remain a second-order issue. It has instigated an impressive series of actions to improve health and health care for the poorest in society. To reduce health inequalities, however, it must reverse trends in the opposite direction. It is unrealistic to expect demonstrable progress at this stage. But without

The NHS is important, but so are measures aimed at keeping people healthy and reducing health inequalities. This should be reflected more clearly in the overall shape and direction of health policy.

stronger political leadership and a higher priority given to measures aimed at reducing inequalities, the chances of significantly reducing health inequalities in the next decade are slim.

Conclusion

The main purpose of this review has been to reflect on what has happened since 1997, rather than advocate future action. Five years is a short time in health policy, so the effects of many new measures, good or bad, would not be detectable at this stage. Even after further time has elapsed it will be difficult to attribute the causes of specific changing health patterns to particular interventions. Our findings suggest that the Government is travelling in the right direction – that is, towards a more robustly funded NHS, improved standards of health and social care, more patient-centred services and a system that is trying to reduce health inequalities. They also point to certain adjustments in style and emphasis that could strengthen and consolidate progress made so far.

First, it is important to keep the money flowing, but any remaining illusions that money alone will save the NHS must be dispelled.

Second, it is time to let go – to curb the incessant flow of orders from the centre. The Government must continue to build the morale and confidence of the workforce, and enable them to take ownership of the reform process.

Third, there should be fewer, but broader targets for the NHS, which are costed and funded appropriately.

Fourth, a better balance should be achieved between health and health care. The NHS is important, but so are measures aimed at keeping people healthy and reducing health inequalities. This should be reflected more clearly in the overall shape and direction of health policy.

Finally, the Government must prepare the public for the long haul. It is time to stop making heroic promises and buckle down to the unglamorous detail of building a good-enough health system for the 21st century.

2 Funding

Key issues:

- Labour's NHS funding record
- International comparisons of health care spending
- Translating spending *inputs* into health care *outputs*

The inheritance

A history of underfunding

If there is one common feature of all health care systems it is their capacity to consume large amounts of money. Difficulties over the NHS budget became apparent just five months after the inception of the service. Its first allocation of £176 million to cover the nine months of 1948 was, Aneurin Bevan had to tell the Cabinet, £50 million short.[1] Virtually every year since, the NHS has received additional funding on top of its planned budget. Health care in the UK now dominates government expenditure, accounting for nearly 28 per cent of all spending, excluding social security payments.[2]

When Labour took office in May 1997, the NHS across the UK had in the previous year received one of the smallest 'real' increases in its budget for many years – a rise of just one tenth of one per cent (after accounting for general inflation in the economy as measured by the GDP deflator). But over the whole of the previous Parliament, spending on the NHS had increased by an average of 2.6 per cent per year in real terms. Over the whole period of the existence of the NHS, the average annual real increase in funding had been just over 3 per cent – marginally ahead of the real growth of the economy as a whole. As Figure 5 also shows, real spending changes since the early 1980s (and, in fact, back to the inception of the NHS) have been very erratic.

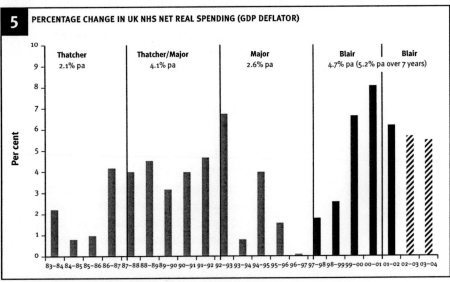

5 PERCENTAGE CHANGE IN UK NHS NET REAL SPENDING (GDP DEFLATOR)

Source: Department of Health Expenditure Plans (various)

Expressions of a willingness to pay more tax did not seem to be translated into a willingness to vote for parties committed to spending more on the NHS.

While Figure 5 presents the official record of real spending, Figure 6 shows the *volume* changes in NHS spending every year – after taking account of inflation as experienced by the NHS itself (rather than the economy as a whole). In general, these annual volume figures were less than the financial resources apparently available after taking account of inflation in the economy.

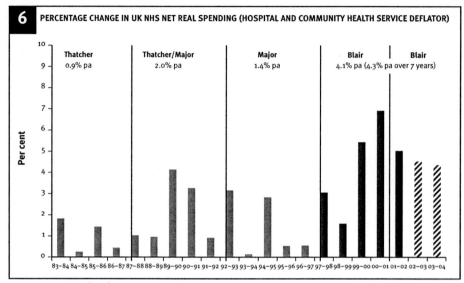

6 PERCENTAGE CHANGE IN UK NHS NET REAL SPENDING (HOSPITAL AND COMMUNITY HEALTH SERVICE DEFLATOR)

Source: Appleby J (1999) Government funding of the UK NHS: What does the historical record reveal? *Journal of Health Service Research & Policy* 4:2; 79–89 (updated for years 98–99 – 03–04).

From the point of view of setting the budget for the NHS, Labour inherited a process that had remained essentially unchanged for many years: bilateral negotiations between the Department of Health and the Treasury over the annual public expenditure survey (PES) produced a budget for the year ahead (together with indications for planned spending a few years into the future).

The public's perspective

Two further perspectives on NHS funding are also worth noting: the views of the public and comparisons with other countries. Opinion poll evidence of the public's view about NHS funding before 1997 was relatively unambiguous – a majority felt the NHS was underfunded and around six in ten stated they would be willing to pay more tax if it were spent on health, education and other social benefits.[3] Of course, as many commentators suggested at the time, these (survey) expressions of a willingness to pay more tax did not seem to be translated into a willingness to vote for parties committed to spending more on the NHS. Nevertheless, economic growth is closely associated internationally with a public desire to spend more on health care. With increasing standards of living in the UK,* it is not surprising to find that opinion polls consistently report the public wish for NHS spending to increase.

Comparisons with other countries

From an international perspective there are two views: in terms of per capita spending on all health care (public and private), in 1997 the UK ranked 11th out of 15 European Union countries (and 9th on public sector spending only). In terms of the share of national income (GDP) devoted to health care, the situation looked worse, with the UK ranking 14th for total spending and 11th on public spending. At the time of the 1997 general election, such figures did not feature very much in public debate about NHS funding. It was only later that NHS funding would be seen in such comparatively unfavourable terms.

---

* For example, male real hourly wages in the UK increasing by over 30 percent in real terms between 1978 and 1996.[4]

The policy pledges

Increasing spending in real terms

The 1997 manifesto stated that '[It is a myth] that the solution to every problem is increased spending...'[5] Nevertheless, it asserted that a Labour Government would implement two pledges. The first commitment was that spending would be increased in real terms (that is, above general inflation in the economy, as measured by the GDP deflator) every year. This extra money would, the manifesto said, be spent on patients not bureaucracy. The indirect commitment was that in the interests of a soundly managed economy, Labour would, for the first two years of office, stick to the previous administration's departmental ceilings for spending.

The commitment to raise spending on the NHS in real terms was, in the absence of any numbers, somewhat minimal; the NHS has almost always received real increases in funding – 1979/80 being the most recent exception (*see* Figure 5).

Matching the EU's spending

On January 16th 2000, the Prime Minister, Tony Blair, was to outline Labour's second manifesto pledge: a commitment to further increases in NHS spending that would, he claimed, see the proportion of the UK's GDP devoted to health care equal the average for the European Union (*see* below). Just over a year later, in the March 2001 Budget, the Chancellor, Gordon Brown, announced that he had asked Derek Wanless to carry out a review to assess demand and cost pressures on the NHS over the next twenty years. This would lead to recommendations for providing financial and other resources to ensure that 'the NHS can provide a publicly funded, comprehensive, high quality service available on the basis of clinical need and not ability to pay'.[6]

Interview transcript from Breakfast with Frost 2000

David Frost:
So what's your message, for instance, to those people, the exceptions to the rule maybe in the sense that the Health Service does a good job for a lot of people of course. But what's your message to Jane Skeet this morning?

Tony Blair:
Well my message is that I accept the responsibility to make sure that the situation that occurred in respect of her mother does not occur, I accept that responsibility, I'm trying to put it right. I have to put it right step-by-step and stage-by-stage, it takes, for example, three years to train a nurse, seven years to train a doctor.
I mean if I can just say to you what over the next few years we will be able to do, if we run the economy properly over the next few years, we've got the first year, as I say, of substantial extra resources for the Health Service going in. Next year is the same, the year after that it's the same. If this July when we work out the next three year period after that three year period we can carry on getting real-term rises in the Health Service of almost five per cent, then at the end of that five years we will be in a position where our Health Service spending comes up to the average of the European Union, it's too low at the moment so we'll bring it up to there.

Source:
http://news.bbc.co.uk/hi/english/static/audio_video/programmes/breakfast_with_frost/transcripts/blair16.jan.txt

Over the Government's first term, real spending increased by 4.7 per cent on average per year.

The Government's actions

Increasing NHS funding

Despite its manifesto commitment to retain the Conservatives' spending limits for health, Labour did, in fact, exceed its departmental ceilings in its first two years. While John Major's Government planned to increase cash spending on the English NHS by 3.2 per cent, Labour increased it by 5.1 per cent. Similarly, in 1998/9, Conservative plans for a cash rise of 2.3 per cent turned out to be 5.6 per cent under Labour.[7]

As Figures 5 and 6 show, subsequent levels of spending officially reached new heights for the NHS across the UK; over the Government's first term, real spending increased by 4.7 per cent on average per year. Taken together with spending plans so far announced, across the seven years from 1997 to 2004, average annual real spending per year should reach 5.2 per cent.

These large sums of money – cash increases totalling over £29 billion between 1996/7 and 2003/4 (a 72 per cent rise) – were mainly reached as part of a new process for setting departmental budgets: the comprehensive spending review (CSR). The first CSR, in 1998, set budgets for the following three years up to 2001/02. It aimed to introduce greater certainty into financial planning: the NHS would know how much money it would receive over three years and be able to plan more effectively and efficiently – unlike the previous system, which led to uncertainties about how much money the NHS would receive each year. The CSR also introduced the notion of public service agreements (PSAs) which, in theory, linked public spending to key Government objectives for each department.

While most departments' CSR budgets were maintained, a few – the Department of Health's in particular – were subject to considerable change. The 2000 Budget, for example, nearly doubled the CSR-determined real increase to the 2000/01 NHS budget by announcing an extra £2 billion. And the 2001 Budget announced an increase of £1 billion over three years – again, on top of increases already announced by the 2000 CSR. Of course, the fact that the CSR has not so far fulfilled one of the Treasury's aims (budget stability for the NHS) because of ad hoc additions to the NHS budget should not, perhaps, be criticised too harshly. Nevertheless, while unexpected additions are better than unexpected subtractions, neither encourage efficient planning.

A presentational feature of the 1998 CSR for the NHS was that the amounts for the three years' budgets were rolled up in a way that grossly overstated the size of the allocated increases: a three-year increase of £21 billion was, in reality, an increase of £9 billion. Such 'triple counting' was heavily criticised at the time – not least by the Treasury Select Committee, which stated that, 'There is...no cash bonanza of the type which newspaper headlines might suggest, but a steady increase in real resources.' The Committee recommended that, 'for the sake of transparency, in future the Government should refer to annual increases over the previous year rather than a cumulative total.'[8] Such triple counting has not, at least for the NHS, occurred since. Nevertheless, there may be some reason to believe that over-enthusiastic announcements of large sums of money – although followed by widespread media attention on the true amounts involved – to an extent fuelled public expectations of improvements that the NHS would find hard to meet.

Pursuing the European average

Presaging the second CSR (scheduled for the summer of 2000) came the Prime Minister's assertion during a television interview that if spending continued to increase at around 5 per cent in real terms, then the UK would be spending the same as the average of the European Union within five years. This was subsequently clarified: spending being defined as *total* spending (public and private) on health care as a proportion of GDP, and the consequent EU average being 8 per cent (of GDP).

Although widely reported as a target, in fact – as the *Breakfast with Frost* interview transcript makes clear – the Prime Minister was merely re-presenting, in a comparative way, the amounts the Government already planned to spend on the NHS. This was presumably designed as a reply to numerous unfavourable comparisons in the media (between, for example, cancer survival rates) that were made between the NHS and other countries' health systems. The implication was that, once UK spending reached the EU average, the UK would also enjoy European levels of health care and, further, European levels of *health*.

While there seems little doubt that UK spending on both public and private health care will reach 8 per cent of GDP by 2005/6, there have been many criticisms of the factual basis concerning the correct measure of the European average spend on health care.[9,10,11] Figure 7, for example, shows the path required if UK health care spending is to reach the Government's own definition of the EU average (ie, 8 per cent of GDP – based on an *un*weighted average of *all* EU countries' percentage spends for 1998, including the UK). However, given past trends, by 2005 other EU countries' spending on health care is likely to be higher than 8 per cent. Trends suggest it will reach around 10.7 per cent based on the mathematically more appropriate measure of a *weighted* average, *excluding* the UK.[12] This implies a much higher level of spending than the government is currently planning – roughly £30 billion more in real terms by 2005/6.

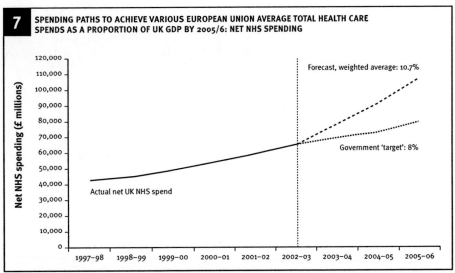

7 SPENDING PATHS TO ACHIEVE VARIOUS EUROPEAN UNION AVERAGE TOTAL HEALTH CARE SPENDS AS A PROPORTION OF UK GDP BY 2005/6: NET NHS SPENDING

Source: King's Fund

Regardless of the disagreements about the correct definition of average and other issues in this context, the Government has made it clear that the aim is total health spending of 8 per cent of GDP.[13] In any case, these arguments have been overtaken by events, in particular the announcement by the Chancellor in the March 2001 Budget that Derek Wanless would be taking a sweeping look at appropriate funding

To date, an extra £18 billion has already been added to the NHS budget since 1997/8. Yet there have been persistent complaints that little has changed in the NHS.

levels for the NHS. In November 2001, Wanless produced an interim report.[14] Its conclusion, after testing a number of financing methods against three criteria (efficiency, equity and patient choice), was that the current system of general taxation would not, in itself, give rise to additional resource pressures, and that it is both fair and efficient,* although it provides rather limited freedom of individual patient choice. These conclusions reinforced evidence put forward in *The NHS Plan* and provided some counterweight to ongoing arguments that general taxation was an unsustainable source of funding.

The final Wanless report – which, presumably, will set out a view about actual resource requirements for the NHS over the next twenty years – is due to be published in 2002.

The impact of policy

Where did all the money go?

Figures 5 and 6 show that the Government should achieve its aim of increasing total health care spending to 8 per cent of GDP by 2005/6. To date, an extra £18 billion has already been added to the NHS budget since 1997/8. Yet there have been persistent complaints that little has changed in the NHS. There is also some evidence that a key area of activity – inpatient and day cases – has not been increasing as fast as might be expected, especially given the extra resources injected into the service (*see* Figure 8). The implication of many media stories has been that the NHS has wasted the extra money. The truth is more complicated – and difficult to uncover.

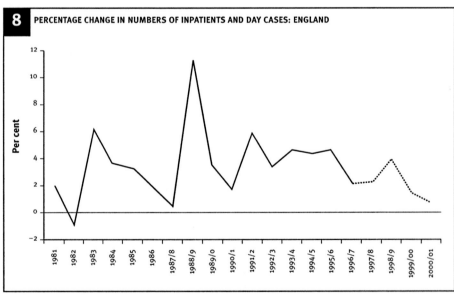

8 PERCENTAGE CHANGE IN NUMBERS OF INPATIENTS AND DAY CASES: ENGLAND

Source: Hospital Episode Statistics

Over the last five years there have been a number of cost and other pressures that have reduced real resources available to the NHS – and potentially its ability to increase activity. For example, NHS-specific inflation (doctors' and nurses' pay rises, etc) has been above rates in the economy as a whole. Dealing with accumulated deficits from previous years has effectively reduced current years' spending as bud-

---

* As the UK tax system is mildly progressive, 'contributions' to the NHS fall more heavily on the rich than the poor. The tax system is also reasonably efficient in terms of the cost of raising money for the NHS. Social and private insurance systems tend to be less efficient due to the administration necessary to collect payments.

gets are brought back into line and creditors paid. And there have been a number of specific cost pressures (such as large increases in employer superannuation contributions, funding the commitment to reduce junior doctors' hours and rising clinical negligence claims). Combined with the extensive earmarking of large amounts of new money through the Health Modernisation Fund, this has resulted in some (non-priority) areas of the NHS being squeezed financially and cost savings having to be made across many services.[15]

More money...but are the public satisfied?

While some of the cost pressures the NHS has experienced over the last few years are likely to be one-off difficulties, there is a more fundamental problem with which all governments struggle: how much *should* be spent on the NHS? The problem for any publicly funded service is that, in the absence of a market in which 'total' spending is decided automatically through the sum of many individual private spending decisions, there are few agreed benchmarks on which to base a decision as to the appropriate level of funding. Yet a decision must be taken and, to an extent, justified.

Historically, decisions about NHS spending levels have been the result of a combination of the technical and the political. The former has in recent decades essentially consisted of taking the previous year's spending levels and building up a new budget based on estimates of need (changes in demographic characteristics, for example), necessary new service developments, and so on. The political input brings in factors such as a government's wider economic goals, which have, in the past, included purposeful reductions in the total share of public spending in the economy. But despite what is a complicated process, setting the NHS budget remains, and must always be, subjective.

Therefore, although there is no 'right' level of spending for the NHS, one indicator that could be used as a proxy to gauge the *appropriateness* of NHS funding levels is public opinion. For example, findings from the British Social Attitudes 2000 survey[16] found that the proportion of people *agreeing* that taxes should be increased and spent on health (and other social programmes) fell from 59 per cent in 1996 to 50 per cent in 2000. One interpretation of this change could be that the increases in NHS spending over this period went some way to satisfying the public's wishes to spend more on the NHS. Similarly, when asked about their overall satisfaction with the NHS, 42 per cent said they were very or fairly satisfied in 2000 compared with 36 per cent in 1996.

The problem with using public opinion as a measure of appropriate health spending, however, is illustrated by the Scottish NHS experience. For many years, total per capita health care spending in Scotland has hovered around the average for the European Union. While this extra spending has purchased more resources – more doctors, nurses, beds, etc – figures from the same survey (author's calculation) suggest that it has not bought higher levels of public satisfaction. In fact, the proportion who are very or fairly satisfied in Scotland (41.8 per cent) is actually lower than for England (43.4 per cent), and the proportion who are very or quite dissatisfied is higher (41 per cent vs 38.5 per cent).

What can the UK afford to spend on health care?

An alternative spending benchmark was, however, implied when the Prime Minister indicated that health care spending levels will rise to match the EU average. Given

But increased funding has come with strings attached. As part of the largesse, the key political message has been that as the politicians have delivered their part of the deal (more money), now it's the turn of the NHS to deliver (and deliver and deliver).

a persistent and strong relationship across countries between the level of per capita wealth (GDP) and the level of health care spending per head (*see*, for example, Figure 9) a possible guide to spending levels is the amount this relationship indicates the UK should *expect* to spend given its wealth.[17] although the UK economy is the fourth largest in the world, as Figure 7 shows, even among EU countries it only ranks 11th in terms of GDP per head. Nevertheless, Figure 7, which uses 1997 data for the EU, suggests that an 'affordable' level of per capita health care spending for the UK was, in 1997, around 18 per cent more than was actually spent. As it happens, expressed as a per centage of GDP, such a spending level is only marginally more than the Government's current target of 8 per cent.

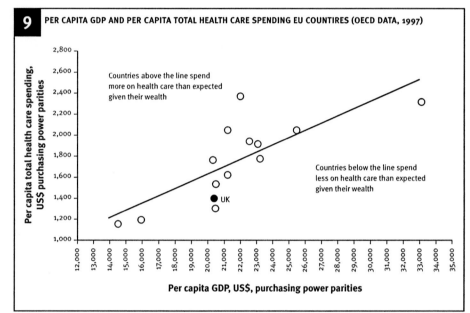

9 PER CAPITA GDP AND PER CAPITA TOTAL HEALTH CARE SPENDING EU COUNTIRES (OECD DATA, 1997)

Source: OECD Health Data File, 2001

Conclusions

Increased funding expectations

Opinion poll findings that people are willing to pay higher taxes to increase NHS funding are commonly criticised on the grounds that when it comes to voting, the electorate leaves its principles at home. Judging by the wording of Labour's 1997 manifesto, this observation was well taken: prudence in public spending, no income tax rises and a rather indistinct commitment to real increases in NHS funding were the pledges. The reality has been somewhat different. Previous Conservative spending plans were exceeded slightly in the first two years, and, since then, significant extra funds have been channelled into the NHS (although, not as much as initial headlines suggested).

But increased funding has come with strings attached. As part of the largesse, the key political message has been that as the politicians have delivered their part of the deal (more money), now it's the turn of the NHS to deliver (and deliver and deliver) on the modernisation programme laid out in *The NHS Plan*. To link extra funding to tangible changes in the NHS is not exceptional: the Treasury, on behalf of taxpayers, naturally wants to know that the NHS has plans to use the money to improve services. But even if the new rate of increase in NHS funding continues, or is exceeded, there remains a dismal economic message: while more money buys more resources – such as doctors, nurses, equipment and buildings – no matter how much is spent on health care, in the long run there will never be enough to satisfy all our demands. Furthermore, the experience of the NHS over the last fifty years, evidence from other countries' health care experiences, and research into the economic peculiarities of health and health care, all suggest that the link between financial inputs and any number of types of outputs (satisfaction, healthiness and so on) is not at all straightforward.

Opaque decision-making over spending

Increased funding will not, of itself, solve all the problems of the NHS. In this sense, the amount that is spent on the NHS is a secondary policy issue. There are two primary issues. The first is the *way* in which decisions on spending are carried out. Rather than the somewhat opaque decision making involved in the comprehensive spending review, a popularly agreed process for arriving at a decision on spending levels, in which trade offs and the necessity for priority-setting are clearly recognised, would lead to a greater public ownership of the eventual spending decision. The work of Derek Wanless and the Treasury Health Trends Team has gone some way down this path, but there is a long way to go, for example, exploring methods to involve the public more closely in budgetary decisions.

Spending and NHS objectives

The second, related, issue is to understand more fully the *links* and relationships between spending and the many objectives of the NHS. Current understanding of these relationships is poor – but without such knowledge the chances of wasting scarce national resources increases. The public service agreements (PSAs) are a step in the right direction, helping to close the tax-spend-outcome loop. But more evidence needs to be generated to reveal more clearly the relative costs and benefits of different PSA targets, and, importantly, to help attribute improvements in the NHS to increased levels of spending.

The verdict

The NHS has received historically significant increases in funding – well above the level of inflation since 1999. Visible evidence of the new money is still hard to find – but this will change if extra investment is maintained. The Government now seems more in step with public wishes to devote more of the nation's wealth to health care. However, fundamental questions about how much money the NHS should get and how it should be spent remain unresolved.

3 Waiting

Key issues:

- Bringing down NHS waiting lists
- Reducing waiting times for elective surgery
- Speeding up access to primary and emergency care

The inheritance

A long history of waiting

The NHS is popularly seen as synonymous with queuing. When it opened its doors for business on the 'appointed day' in 1948, it immediately inherited a waiting list. Over half a million people were waiting for admission to hospital in 1950. By the 1980s numbers reached over three quarters of a million, and today they are just over one million. For many, the waiting list record is seen as a depressing indictment of the NHS. It has posed a real policy challenge to all governments.

Labour's inheritance in 1997 consisted of not only the numerical – numbers waiting, time spent waiting and so on – but also a long history of policy initiatives stretching back to the 1950s designed to deal with waiting.

Initiatives to reduce the numbers waiting for admission to hospital included:

- A guidance by the Ministry of Health in the 1960s on managing lists and advice to GPs on gaining admission for their patients.
- In 1975, further guidance was issued on managing lists, and special funding was devoted to dealing with supply 'bottlenecks'.
- The 1979 Royal Commission on the NHS[1] focused attention on waiting times as opposed to list length – but was unable to offer any instant solutions.
- During the 1980s, the waiting list – later to become waiting times – initiative combined special funding (£252 million by the time it ended in 1995) with targeted efforts at reducing the longest lists and waiting times.[2]
- By the mid-1990s waits of over two years had virtually disappeared – but lists had got longer. The internal market reforms of the early 1990s were also an attempt to, at a minimum, equalise waiting times around the country through the purchasing decisions of health authorities and GP fundholders.

Statistically, Labour inherited an inpatient and day case waiting list of nearly 1.2 million people – the highest it had been since 1948 (see Figure 10). Across England, around 2 percent of the entire population was on a waiting list. But these national figures masked variations between different areas of the country (and particularly between consultants). The number of people waiting for hospital admission per 1,000 head of population varied as much as four-fold across the country, and outpatient lists varied by as much as forty-fold between the best and the worst

The key concern for patients is not the number of people in front of them but the speed with which the queue moves.

health authorities. Such differences have been a persistent feature – but their causes have generally defied explanation.

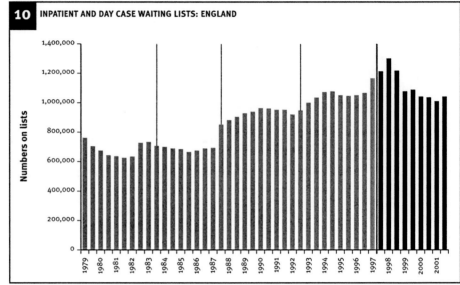

10 INPATIENT AND DAY CASE WAITING LISTS: ENGLAND

Source: Department of Health

Numbers waiting on lists suggests an ordered, first-come, first-served supermarket checkout queue. But *the key* concern for patients is not the number of people in front of them but the speed with which the queue moves. Policy initiatives pre-1997 had in fact achieved some success in reducing waiting *times* for admission to hospital (*see* Figure 11). In March 1997, the average waiting time for hospital admission was just over four months, with half of all patients (the median) being admitted within three months.

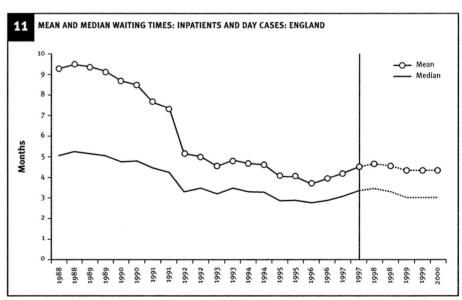

11 MEAN AND MEDIAN WAITING TIMES: INPATIENTS AND DAY CASES: ENGLAND

Source: Department of Health

While a majority of patients were admitted to hospital within three to four months, and despite successful attempts to cut the number of very long waits, by 1997 there were still over 42,000 patients waiting longer than a year.

From a patient's point of view, waiting begins with their GP's referral to outpatients. In March 1997, around 3 percent of patients had waited over six months by the time of their appointment, with 83 percent having waited less than three months. These figures were part of a relatively unchanging trend in outpatient waiting times since 1994 – when national information was first collected.

The policy pledges

Cutting waiting lists and times

Before 1997, policies on waiting had begun by focusing on reducing the numbers of people on lists and then moved on to tackling waiting times. Labour's 1997 manifesto [3] reversed this policy pendulum – at least for the headline-grabbing inpatient waiting list – with a pledge to cut the *number* of people waiting by 100,000 by the end of that Parliament. This reduction represented a cut of just under 9.5 percent in the size of the total waiting list. To be fair, waiting *times* were not completely ignored: the manifesto also pledged '[to] end waiting for cancer surgery, thereby helping thousands of women waiting for breast cancer treatment.' Although not mentioned in the manifesto, the new Government continued with the previous administration's Patients' Charter commitments of a maximum inpatient waiting time of 18 months.

Following these pledges, further commitments to reduce waiting lists and times were announced:

- December 1997: The White Paper, *The New NHS*,[4] stated that the original manifesto pledge to cut cancer waiting times would be set as a target, and that by April 2000 no patient with suspected breast cancer would wait more than two weeks to see a specialist following an urgent referral by their GP. This target was rolled out between April and December 2000 to cover all cancers.

- August 1999: As numbers on outpatient lists waiting over 13 weeks reached nearly half a million, the Department of Health announced a performance fund to tackle long outpatient waits. Locally negotiated agreements targeting specialties with excessive waits were agreed, and, by March 2000, numbers waiting over 13 weeks were to be reduced to 334,000 across the country.

- July 2000: *The NHS Plan*[5] extended the 'war on waiting' with the announcement of a bewildering array of targets covering not only inpatient and outpatient waiting lists but waiting in accident and emergency departments, and waiting for GP appointments and other primary care professionals.

- September 2000: *The NHS Cancer Plan*[6] extended targets for waiting times for people with cancer with no one to wait more than four weeks from diagnosis to treatment for a variety of cancers, including breast cancer, testicular cancer, children's cancers, leukaemia.

While these new targets (*see* Table 2 for a complete list since 1997) represented another swing of the policy pendulum back towards tackling waiting times, the original 1997 pledge to cut inpatient lists by 100,000 was retained. *The NHS Plan* also announced a need to increase the number of 'booked' appointments and admissions.

Between 1998/9 and 2000/01, over £737 million was allocated to health authorities and trusts for specific actions to reduce lists and times.

The Government's actions

Earmarked funding

As with previous waiting list initiatives, policy over the last five years to reduce lists and times has been supported in a variety of ways. Earmarked funding – via the Health Modernisation Fund – has been set aside to tackle targets: between 1998/9 and 2000/01, over £737 million was allocated to health authorities and trusts for specific actions to reduce lists and times.

Investing resources and management

Guidance and best practice on dealing with waiting lists has also been published. And special teams (such as the National Patients Access Team, the Waiting List Action Team and the Task Force) have been set up to help individual trusts address their waiting list problems. Overall, considerable resource and management effort has been focused on meeting the various targets set by Government.

Table 1 details the Department of Health's headline reporting of the war on waiting.

Table 1: Government press releases on waiting lists: May 1997–January 2002[*]

1997/351	Frank Dobson announces action on waiting lists and times
1998/495	Waiting lists plummet by nearly 30,000 in one month
1998/562	Waiting lists fall by further 20,000 – waiting times fall for five months in a row
1998/064	Waiting list pledges will be delivered – says Frank Dobson
1998/101	'NHS waiting lists will be shorter by April next year' says Frank Dobson
1998/125	NHS delivers 18-month waiting list pledge – nobody waiting more than 18 months for treatment
1998/166	Government gets tough on waiting list targets – list buster appointed to head new team
1998/200	NHS delivers Government's 18-month waiting list pledge
1998/270	The supertanker has turned – Dobson
1998/281	Frank Dobson comments on waiting lists
1998/349	Waiting lists fall by 45,000 – supertankers turns – NHS waiting lists falling faster than ever before
1998/405	Dobson signals another fall in waiting lists
1998/415	Waiting lists down again by record 24,000 August – fall in numbers waiting over one year
1999/0007	Record 31,000 monthly fall in NHS waiting lists
1999/0118	NHS waiting lists fall by 14,200 in January
1999/0184	Record 39,700 drop in waiting lists delivers NHS promise one month early
1999/0278	Dobson hails biggest waiting list fall yet as NHS delivers even more than promised
1999/0332	Waiting lists rise but still 65,000 lower than target – Frank Dobson
1999/0420	Waiting list figures at end of May
1999/0492	Waiting list figures at end of June
1999/0512	John Denham announces £30 million to step up war on NHS waiting
1999/0517	Hospital acts against waiting list irregularities

[*] Note: Press releases selected using the Department of Health search engine on the basis of the words 'waiting list' in the title or first paragraph of press release text. Statistical press releases were excluded.

Table 1: *contd.*

1999/0528	Tough new monitoring regime for outpatients unveiled as new weapon in the war on NHS waiting
1999/0601	Waiting lists fall again
1999/0659	Waiting lists continue to fall
1999/0696	Rise in outpatient waiting times slows as more patients are seen
1999/0709	Inpatient waiting lists continue to fall
2000/0090	Fall in outpatient waiting lists
2000/0202	Waiting lists fall
2000/0284	Meeting waiting list target is 'work in progress'
2000/0328	Waiting lists stay below target
2000/0398	Waiting lists stay below target
2000/0469	Action team to go into hospitals failing on waiting
2000/0505	Milburn orders 'go for growth' on NHS beds: waiting lists fall again
2000/0562	NHS waiting lists continue to fall
2000/0643	Waiting times and lists continue to fall as modernisation programme bites
2001/0022	Fall in waiting lists continues
2001/0066	Steady progress in the war on waiting
2001/0181	New schemes cut cancer waiting times as waiting lists fall across the board
2001/0307	NHS waiting lists still over 100,000 less than March 1997
2001/0377	All aspects of NHS waiting improved since last year
2001/0410	Over 90 percent of urgent cancer referrals seen within two weeks
2001/0459	Drop in number of patients waiting over a year for treatment
2001/0529	Further progress towards reducing waiting times
2001/0605	Real progress on waiting times, but real challenges ahead: Hutton
2001/0629	Waiting list manipulation is unacceptable
2002/0016	Two thirds of all trusts have no inpatients waiting over 15 months

The impact of policy

Table 2 summarises the position regarding all waiting list targets and pledges announced since 1997. The overall picture is mixed: some targets have been achieved; some have been missed; while for others there is still some time to go before the target is to be met.

Getting the waiting list down

The key 1997 manifesto target – to reduce the total inpatient waiting list by 100,000 –appears to have been successful – and over a year before the end of the last Parliament. As Figure 12 shows, however, one year on from the baseline date of March 1997, waiting lists had increased to nearly 1.3 million – so reducing lists to 100,000 below the March 1997 level ultimately required a cut of around 240,000 in numbers waiting. But such cuts were perhaps not all they seemed.

Achievement at local level was patchy. As Figure 13 shows, six out of ten health authorities failed to reduce lists by as much as the average target reduction of 9.5 percent. Of these, nearly one fifth saw their lists increase.

Table 2: Waiting list targets (and milestones) announced since 1997

TARGET	ANNOUNCED?	BY?	ACHIEVED?	COMMENTS
Cut inpatient waiting lists by 100,000 from March 1997 level	May 1997 (1997 manifesto)	End of 1997 Parliament	✓	Achieved by March 2000. But National Audit Office queried 'auditability' of the target [7]
No one with suspected breast cancer to wait more than 2 weeks for outpatient appointment following urgent GP referral	April 2000 (The New NHS)		✗	Latest quarterly figures for September 2001 show over 1,400 women waiting more than 2 weeks
Numbers of outpatients waiting more than 13 weeks to be cut to 334,000	August 1999	March 2000	✗	Substantial cut – from 512,000 to 400,000 – but target missed
No one to wait more than 4 weeks for treatment for testicular cancer, children's cancers and leukaemia following an urgent GP referral	September 2000 (NHS Cancer Plan)	December 2001	?	Information only available in April 2002
No one to wait more than 4 weeks for treatment for breast cancer following diagnosis	September 2000 (NHS Cancer Plan)	December 2001	?	Information only available in April 2002
No one with suspected cancer to wait more than 2 weeks for their first outpatient appointment for patients referred urgently	July 2000 (NHS Plan)	December 2000	✗	Latest quarterly figures for September 2001 show over 6,454 people waiting more than 2 weeks
Reduce number of those waiting over 12 months for inpatient treatment	July 2000 (NHS Plan)	March 2002	**Probably on target**	Numbers fell between September 2000 and March 2001 by 7,000. December 2001 show further falls of 13,200
No one to wait more than 15 months for inpatient treatment	July 2000 (NHS Plan)	March 2002	?	'On target. 66 percent of trusts meeting target as at December 2001', DoH, personal communication
No one to wait more than 6 months for inpatient treatment	July 2000 (NHS Plan)	March 2005	**Not on target?**	Fell between September 2000 and March 2001 by 29,000, but rose by 13,000 to 277,500 in December 2001
No one to wait more than 26 weeks for an outpatient appointment	July 2000 (NHS Plan)	March 2002	**Not on target**	Fell between September 2000 and March 2001, but rose by 2,500, to 84,300 in December 2001
Reduce the number of over 13 week outpatient waiters	July 2000 (NHS Plan)	March 2002	**Not on target?**	Fell between September 2000 and March 2001 by 152,000, but rose by 77,200 to 361,000 in December 2001
No one to wait more than 13 weeks for an outpatient appointment	July 2000 (NHS Plan)	March 2005		
Maintain the commitment to cut waiting lists by 100,000 from March 1997 level	July 2000 (NHS Plan)	Ongoing	✓	But National Audit Office queried 'auditability' of the target
All patients attending A&E to wait 4 hours or less from arrival to admission, transfer or discharge	July 2000 (NHS Plan)	March 2004	?	'On target. 77 percent of trusts meeting target as at December 2001'. DoH, personal communication
No patients to wait no more than 24 hours for an appointment with a primary health care professional and no more than 48 hours for an appointment with a GP	July 2000 (NHS Plan)	March 2004	?	Target changed to 'next working day' and 'next available appointment'. 'On line to be achieved' – DoH personal communication

Source: Department of Health

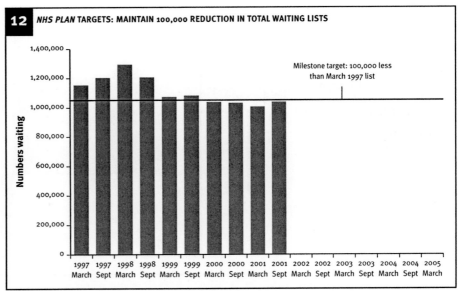

12 *NHS PLAN* **TARGETS: MAINTAIN 100,000 REDUCTION IN TOTAL WAITING LISTS**

Source: Department of Health

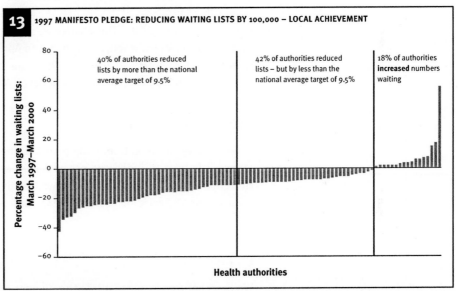

13 **1997 MANIFESTO PLEDGE: REDUCING WAITING LISTS BY 100,000 – LOCAL ACHIEVEMENT**

Source: Department of Health

More importantly, there were problems concerning the way in which lists were reduced and the veracity of national waiting list statistics. The National Audit Office[8] has noted that 46 percent of trust chief executives responding to their survey stated that during 1999/2000 they had redefined the way they counted inpatients. This included reclassifying patients who would previously have been included on waiting lists as *planned* cases. Planned cases include patients given dates for a course of inpatient treatment such as chemotherapy. Importantly, these cases are not counted as part of the waiting list. In nearly nine out of ten cases this sort of reclassification led to a reduction in total numbers waiting.

This change in classification is, to an extent, reflected in Hospital Episode Statistics (HES) for the period 1997/8–2000/2001. These show that, in terms of source of admission to hospital, numbers of patients admitted from the waiting list or as booked admissions *fell* between 1997 and 2001; the increase in the number of (non-waiting list) planned cases making up over 87 percent of the increase in *all* hospital admissions – including emergencies and maternity cases (*see* Figure 14).

As more and more patients crowd into progressively shorter waits, it will become increasingly difficult to cut the longest waits.

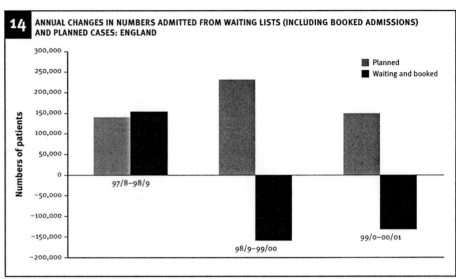

14 ANNUAL CHANGES IN NUMBERS ADMITTED FROM WAITING LISTS (INCLUDING BOOKED ADMISSIONS) AND PLANNED CASES: ENGLAND

Source: Hospital Episode Statistics

Other changes during 1999/2000 included reclassifying day cases as outpatients. In virtually all instances of this change, the NAO found that it led, again, to a reduction in inpatient waiting lists. This change was graphically illustrated by movements in waiting lists in Wales, when, in February and April 2001, 4,300 endoscopy inpatients (6 percent of the total list) were removed from the inpatient waiting list. This led to a claimed reduction of 1,300 waiting between March 1997 and April 2001.[9]

Reducing waiting times

In terms of achievement, as Table 2 shows, the picture is mixed. For a number of targets it is hard to judge success or failure as routine data is not yet available. However, on the five main groups of waiting list targets – inpatients, outpatients, cancer patients, accident and emergency and primary care – some information is available:

Inpatients

While recent trends suggest that the number of people waiting over 12 months is increasing, indications from the Department of Health (personal communication) are that the NHS is on course to ensure that, by March 2002, no one waits more than 15 months (*see* Figure 15). However, although there are still three years to go before the deadline looms for eradicating waiting over six months, recent trends are in the wrong direction.

Overall, this 'bunching up' of the waiting list distribution is to be expected: as long waits are squeezed, the numbers waiting shorter periods of time (between 6 and 12 months) will grow. The question is whether the squeeze can push waiting times back to the target maximum of six months by 2005. As more and more patients crowd into progressively shorter (but longer than six-month) waits, it will become increasingly difficult to cut the longest waits. A concern will be the ability of the NHS to increase its level of activity in order to get patients through the system fast enough to make headway into the waiting list. Recent increases in inpatient and day case activity have been surprisingly small – averaging around 2 percent a year since 1997/8, but in 2000/01 only increasing by 0.8 percent. This is certainly too low to do much more than stand still given demand pressures, let alone reduce the number of people waiting over six months.

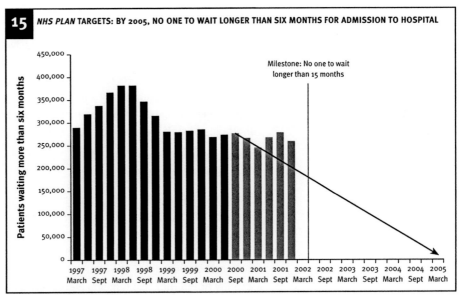

15 *NHS PLAN* TARGETS: BY 2005, NO ONE TO WAIT LONGER THAN SIX MONTHS FOR ADMISSION TO HOSPITAL

Source: Department of Health

Outpatients

Recent trends in waiting times for outpatients are not encouraging. Having failed on an early target to cut the numbers waiting over 13 weeks to 334,000 (although a substantial cut was made), *The NHS Plan* targets to ensure no one waits more than 26 weeks and to reduce further the number waiting over 13 weeks (on the way to a target of no one waiting over 13 weeks) are not on track (*see* Figure 16). To meet the 26-week target, for example, would require a reduction in numbers waiting of 84,000 between December 2001 and March 2002. A cut of such scale has never been achieved since outpatient waiting list figures have been recorded.

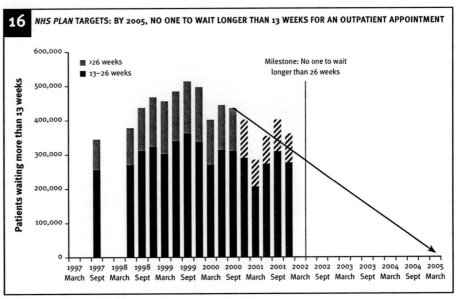

16 *NHS PLAN* TARGETS: BY 2005, NO ONE TO WAIT LONGER THAN 13 WEEKS FOR AN OUTPATIENT APPOINTMENT

Source: Department of Health

One of the difficulties with outpatient targets is that they may suffer some knock-on consequences as a result of local strategies to meet inpatient targets. When, for example, clinical effort and resources are concentrated on dealing with inpatient targets, the movement of patients from outpatient lists to inpatient lists could be constrained.

Cancer patients

Of the waiting time targets for cancer patients, two have been missed and information on two others – a maximum wait of four weeks for treatments for breast cancer and a number of other cancers following an urgent GP referral – is currently unavailable. The NHS Modernisation Board's first Annual Report [10] indicated that these latter two targets are unlikely to have been met for breast cancer and testicular cancer due to shortages of staff and equipment in radiology, pathology and radiotherapy.

Accident and Emergency

The key *NHS Plan* A&E waiting time target – that all patients will wait less than four hours before admission, transfer or discharge – is set to be achieved by March 2004. While there are no regular published statistics to monitor this target, the Department of Health says that over three quarters of trusts had already achieved the target by December 2001 (personal communication). The Audit Commission has recently noted that this target is a step forward from the previous Patients' Charter targets for waiting times in A&E – but that it still needs refinement. [11] Crucially, the three types of patients (those admitted, transferred or discharged) need to be identified separately. This is because 80 percent of A&E patients are discharged, and could mask any indication of performance in the measure of admission within four hours, which is harder to achieve. In other words, targets can be met by increasing the speed of discharge rather than speed of admission.

Primary care

Although the Modernisation Board's Annual Report states that over 60 per cent of practices are already meeting the March 2004 target that no patient should wait more than 24 hours to see a primary care professional and no more than 48 hours to see their GP, it also reports that many areas are having problems. Moreover, the target has been subtly changed, with the substitution of 'next working day' and 'next available appointment' for the 24- and 48-hour limits. As with some other targets there is no standard system for monitoring, but the Department of Health says that the target is on line to be achieved (personal communication).

Conclusions

Waiting lists: the wrong target

Given the findings of the National Audit Office report detailing inappropriate adjustments to NHS waiting lists by many trusts [12] the 1997 manifesto target may remain 'unauditable'. This would be a grave situation in most circumstances; however, there was a more fundamental problem with the pledge to reduce waiting lists: it was the wrong thing to do in the first place. The Prime Minister's defence of the pledge* – equating waiting lists with queues to get into a football ground – failed to recognise that waiting lists do not operate as simple queues: for any individual patient, the *length* of the waiting list is not a good indicator of how *long* they will have to wait.

---

* 'I know that some people think it [reduction of inpatient waiting lists by 100,000] was a foolish pledge. But to those in any doubt, the length of the waiting list does matter. If you are waiting to get through a turnstile into a football ground...you go the one with the shortest queue!' (Speech by the Prime Minister on outpatient waiting lists, September 1999).

Over half of a sample of consultants responding to an NAO survey said that they had treated some routine patients in preference to more urgent cases to reduce waiting list numbers.

A further criticism of the original manifesto pledge was that while it encouraged consultants to increase their workloads, it did so in a way that could mean concentrating on less difficult and, perhaps, less urgent cases. Over half of a sample of consultants responding to an NAO survey said that they had treated some routine patients in preference to more urgent cases to reduce waiting list numbers. However, the extent to which such apparent distortions in clinical priority should be considered a failing is difficult to judge. Although there is a general principle that patients should be treated in order of their clinical priority – the most urgent first and so on – there are also good reasons for consultants to operate in a more flexible way: solely treating the most urgent can mean that some routine patients are never seen or that operating theatres are not used as efficiently as they might be in terms of maximising the time they are in use.

However, A deeper problem lies with the general principle of clinical priority. Crudely put, one consultant's 'urgent' case can be another's 'routine' case. Although such variation in clinical judgement has repeatedly been shown to exist, there has been, and remains, little or no concerted policy attempt to deal with this source of 'distortion' of priorities.

As *The NHS Plan* and subsequent policy documents made clear, while the 100,000 reduction target was to remain in force, there was a distinct policy switch to waiting times. Yet these new targets could be subject to similar criticisms concerning the distortion of clinical priorities. Many of the examples of treating routine patients in preference to urgent cases involved the old Patients' Charter target of a maximum waiting time of 18 months for inpatients (a hangover from previous Conservative policy). And the same problems could be said to arise from the NHS Plan targets, which impose progressively shorter maximum waits over time. Again, however, the extent to which such distortions in clinical priority should be considered a failing is difficult to judge.

Waiting times: a better target?

While there appear to be problems with many of the waiting times targets set since 1997 – both in terms of achievement nationally and the variable achievement at local level – an improvement in policy terms has been the switch to focusing on waiting *times* and, in some areas, a refinement in the type of waiting actually measured and set as targets. Importantly, there has also been a lessening of the obsession with waiting at the acute hospital stage of admission and a recognition of the broader issue of access to care across the whole system – including outpatients, accident and emergency, and primary care.

More fundamentally, waiting list policy over the last five years – and over the last half century – has been based on the presumption that waiting is a bad thing and that if only the supply side of the health care system could be changed in the right way – more money, doctors, beds, better pathways into care and so on – then waiting could be reduced if not, to all intents and purposes, eradicated. But while no government has openly acknowledged the fact (in a system where the usual market mechanisms for rationing are, for good reason, absent) waiting serves an important, and vital, function. Waiting lists essentially act as the key device to bring together supply and demand in the NHS. But they operate in a comparatively crude and uncoordinated way.

The theoretical and ethical case for a method of organising waiting lists (involving, for example, priority scoring systems) in a way that explicitly recognises their rationing function – as well as their implications for equity and efficiency in the NHS – has been made before.[13] There have also been many suggestions for how such methods might work and the criteria that might be applied.[14,15] More recently, examples of scoring systems from other countries have also been described.[16]

Despite such analysis, the main policy failure since the inception of the NHS, and one that remains an urgent priority, has been the lack of any development of a *systematic* method to control and regulate waiting across the whole health care system, as part of a continued effort to keep waiting times within reasonable limits.

The verdict

Policies on waiting for NHS treatment threaten to distort clinical priorities and divert management energies. Although reducing the time people wait for health care is an important policy goal in its own right, a more evidence-based and systematic approach to controlling waiting is required.

4 Rationing

Key issues:

- Labour's role in NHS priority-setting
- The National Institute for Clinical Excellence
- The focus on cancer and heart disease in Government policy

The inheritance

The inevitability of trade-offs

Some people may think that rationing doesn't, or shouldn't, happen in the NHS. Unpalatable as it may be, the fact is that rationing in the NHS has been, and will remain, unavoidable. Demand will *always* outstrip supply, with the consequence that potentially beneficial care will be denied. Even when funding is increasing, decisions about how these new resources are used involve difficult choices between alternatives.

With ability to pay for health care rightly taken out of the equation, the main ways in which health care has been rationed in the NHS are:

- Deterrence: patients are discouraged from making their demands known, for example by reception staff in GP surgeries filtering out some patients
- Deflection: patients are referred to other agencies, for example from the NHS to social services
- Dilution: a reduction in standards or scope of a service
- Delay: waiting lists.[1]

Despite these complexities, before 1997 there had been little effort to address or improve the means by which rationing decisions were made. They were mainly made at a local level, resulting in great variability in health service provision[2] and regional disparities in access to and utilisation of services – popularly known as 'postcode rationing'.

A lack of priority-setting guidance

Further, the means by which these decision were made was largely *implicit,* often hidden in clinical decisions.[3] No mechanism existed to guide priority-setting or to ensure consistency in the way that resource allocation between services was dealt with across the country.

While a lively academic debate about rationing took place before 1997, it appears not to have been translated into an active policy concern or a commitment to tackling rationing head-on at a national level. Notwithstanding the absence of a coherent national policy, there were *some* attempts at explicit rationing emerging immediately before 1997. Examples include the Department of Health excluding some medicines (such as proprietary cough remedies) from NHS prescription[4] – an example of rationing by excluding a category of good or service; and, further back in NHS history, the introduction of charges for dentistry and optometry[5] – rationing by introducing (partial) charges to choke off 'excess' demand.

Rationing and the internal market

Concerns about rationing were largely peripheral to the principal motivations underpinning the introduction of the internal market by the Conservative Government. However, records of a discussion on rationing health care in the House of Commons show that the then Secretary of State believed that 'the internal market would allocate resources better'.[6] Some independent commentators agreed: the purchaser-provider split meant that health authorities were faced with the task of making the best use of their budgets to improve the health of their populations, creating an opportunity to base decisions on systematic analysis rather than processes that largely reinforced the status quo.[7]

Some purchasers *did* respond to this challenge by initiating explicit rationing procedures using a variety of methods including questionnaire surveys, focus groups, health panels and public meetings.[8] For example, the West Glamorgan Health Authority set up a Local Ethics Committee concerned with 'ethical issues arising out of resource allocation and other health care policy decisions.' Around a fifth of authorities reported using cost per 'quality adjusted life year' (QALY) evidence to assist decision-making, with still others planning to do so.[9] Some GP fundholders set up public consultation groups to help set treatment priorities. A number of health authorities were reported, controversially, to have issued guidance that certain minor surgical procedures (eg, the extraction of symptom-less wisdom teeth) were no longer to be treated on the NHS.[10]

Other health authorities, however, were the subject of fierce media criticism for their handling of what were perceived to be rationing questions. High-profile debates of this kind, especially that of Child B, the child who was refused possible life-saving treatment for leukaemia by Cambridge and Huntingdon Health Authority, damaged the Government.

The policy pledges

Neither the term nor the concept of rationing is politically appealing, so it is no surprise to find little mention of it in political manifestos of any kind. Where priorities *are* mentioned, these are couched in the upbeat language of conditions or services targeted to receive additional funding (rather than the flip side of this: of services *not* to receive priority).

Investing in priority conditions

Labour's 1997 manifesto made no mention of resource allocation or rationing;[11] but *The NHS Plan*[12] set out a number of particular conditions – cancer, heart disease and mental health – to receive priority. Labour's 2001 general election manifesto re-emphasised specific conditions: cancer, heart disease and stroke were marked out to receive priority for 'investment and reform': £1 billion earmarked extra funding by 2004, aimed at preventing 300,000 avoidable deaths over the next decade.[13]

Labour has succeeded in putting into place the single most significant attempt at explicit rationing in NHS history.

Tackling postcode prescribing

Both the 2001 manifesto and *The NHS Plan* mention the role of the National Institute of Clinical Excellence (NICE), announced in 1998 as part of the White Paper, *The New NHS: Modern, dependable,*[14] in tackling postcode prescribing. Both documents stated their intention to tackle the 'lottery of care' by directing health authorities and trusts to fund drugs and treatments recommended by NICE.[15]

The Government's actions

Setting out the 'top priorities'

A common rationing strategy used by both past and present governments has been to set priorities largely by identifying and selecting specific 'high-need' *conditions* (as opposed to *services*) – cancer, heart disease and stroke in Labour's case – to receive special attention and earmarked funding.

As the public sector becomes more and more subject to central direction, these priorities have a direct bearing on NHS rationing decisions: measures of performance, such as the new star ratings system, feed directly on the Government's targets. At the top level, Labour has set out a series of contracts called Public Service Agreements between the Treasury and the spending ministries, including the Department of Health. These aim to improve the quality and efficiency of public services and are linked to the Treasury's three-year Spending Reviews. The Department of Health, in turn, has Priorities and Planning Frameworks, which link its targets to performance ratings of NHS institutions, and directives concerning the use of extra money from the Health Modernisation Fund. Thus priorities at the top level flow down into a raft of spending imperatives at the local level. Beyond this, however, ministers have avoided specific rationing decisions.

Establishing NICE

Labour has succeeded in putting into place the single most significant attempt at explicit rationing in NHS history. Since its establishment in April 1999, the National Institute for Clinical Excellence has embarked on an ambitious programme of technical appraisal and guidance. Its remit, set out shortly before it began work, was to 'improve standards of patient care, and to reduce inequities in access to innovative treatment, by establishing a process which will:

- Identify those new treatments and products which are likely to have a significant impact on the NHS, or which for other reasons would benefit from the issue of national guidance at an early stage
- Enable evidence of clinical and cost effectiveness to be brought together to inform a judgement on the value of the treatment relative to alternative uses of resources in the NHS
- Result in the issue of guidance on whether the treatment can be recommended for routine use in the NHS (and if so under what conditions or for which groups of patients) together with a summary of the evidence on which the recommendation is based
- Avoid any significant delays to those sponsoring the innovation either in meeting any national or international regulatory requirements or in bringing the innovation to market in the UK.'[16]

Before NICE could be established, however, a high-profile case in 1999 forced the Government to show its hand on NHS rationing issues. When the impotence drug Viagra was licensed for use in the UK, the Department of Health decided to restrict access to it immediately. In temporary guidance from the Department of Health, doctors were told that the drug could only be made available to patients with a list of pre-existing conditions causing them to suffer from erectile dysfunction – not for all patients who asked for it. In many respects this was a political landmark in the history of the NHS.[17,18] Although not the first time a specific treatment had been excluded, the decision was notable both in terms of the process underpinning it (using evidence on costs and effectiveness) and the recognition, in announcing the decision, of the trade-offs between funding Viagra and other services.

In response, the manufacturers of Viagra successfully took legal action against the Government. They argued that a temporary ban on the drug was unlawful because the Government had not gone through the normal process for placing Viagra on its list of restricted treatments (known as Schedule 11). As a result, the judge agreed that the Government's actions overrode doctors' 'professional judgement', forcing ministers to clarify that their guidance was not binding on the NHS.

The impact of policy

NICE's remit

To date, NICE has published 31 guidance reports. The recommendations of each (and the evidence on cost-effectiveness and net cost impact on the NHS) are summarised in Table 3. NICE has recommended against use in four instances, with a subsequent change of judgement on one – zanamivir (the flu drug, also known as Relenza).[19] A challenging programme of technical appraisals is planned for the future: 28 in 2002 alone.[20] The role of NICE has subsequently been strengthened by making implementation of its guidance mandatory from 2002.

Since its establishment, NICE has embarked on an ambitious programme of technical appraisal and guidance. It arguably represents the most rigorous and *transparent* example of priority-setting internationally. For the first time, the NHS has a systematic, defensible and consistent means of appraising and responding to new health care technologies and their associated demand pressures.

The annual net cost of implementing the guidance NICE had issued by March 2001 is estimated to be between £200–214 million (less than 0.5 per cent of annual spending on the NHS).[21] Guidance issued subsequently suggests a further net cost of between £57 million and £71 million annually. There are, however, problems in constructing these estimates with precision, and they should be treated with caution.

While NICE has said 'yes' more often than 'no' to the technologies it has considered, in most cases the 'yes' is qualified by specified conditions – such as which patients are most likely to benefit. This has required detailed guidelines covering the range of treatment options for different patient groups – an evolving function that is both important and, given the magnitude of the task and often patchy evidence, challenging.[22]

It was this particular issue – the lack of evidence on benefit to particular patient groups – which led to controversy over NICE's appraisal of the multiple sclerosis (MS) drug, beta interferon, late in 2001. In the absence of evidence, NICE assessed costs and benefits for *all* patients, resulting in a technical appraisal suggesting it to

Without ring-fenced money to pay the costs of adopting NICE guidance, the implementation of such an obligation will have to be funded by cutting other services.

be unfavourable on cost-effectiveness grounds. The Department of Health subsequently announced it will conduct a large-scale 'experiment', whereby beta interferon will be available to all patients, allowing the collection of evidence and the identification of which patients for whom it *might* be cost-effective.

Cost effectiveness evidence has no 'absolute' interpretation – considering whether a treatment with a given cost per QALY (or other measure of health gain) is good value for money or not relies on comparison of this evidence with that for other services that are already funded, or against a benchmark known as a 'threshold'.

Guidelines issued by NICE to date *imply* a threshold in the range of £20,000 to £30,000.[23] Statements made at the annual meeting of NICE suggested a *de facto* threshold of £30,000 [24] though the very existence of threshold has been strenuously denied by NICE. However, cost-effectiveness is not the only factor considered in issuing guidance. For example, NICE decided in favour of Riluzole for motor neurone disease, despite a cost per QALY gained of between £34,000 and £43,500, stating that the committee took account of 'the severity and relatively short life span' of patients and 'the value patients attached' to the extension in survival.

The issue of what the threshold is or should be is complicated by lack of evidence on the effects of treatment on quality of life. As Table 3 demonstrates, it is often not possible to measure health gain in terms of QALYs, so other measures are used instead (such as life years gained). This suggests that *multiple* thresholds operate simultaneously.

A further controversy about NICE's work concerns the role of patients in its decision-making processes. Many patient groups have complained that NICE takes too little account of their views and that its 'quality of life' measures are inadequate. Many have called for a greater role in NICE's appraisal process. In responding to these concerns, however, NICE may be at risk of a bias towards patients whose conditions are covered by well-organised lobby groups.

It is still unclear how NICE guidance is implemented locally. For example, guidance issued in favour of Riluzole may be interpreted in one area as an additional service for patients with MND (and resources taken from other treatment areas); in others, Riluzole may be funded but support services for MND patients withdrawn. This means that the effect both on MND patients and those with other illnesses may still vary from one area to another. To some extent, this is beneficial, because it allows NHS bodies to respond to local needs, but it does mean that Labour cannot claim to have ironed out all variations in health care resource use through NICE.

In 2001, the Government announced its commitment to ensure that patients receive drugs and treatments recommended by NICE, with a promise that it will place primary care trusts under a statutory obligation to provide appropriate funding for recommended treatments. But commentators have pointed out that, without ring-fenced money to pay the costs of adopting NICE guidance, the implementation of such an obligation will have to be funded by cutting other services. Local decisions about such cuts will be very different and variations in quality of care between different parts of the country will arise. Evidence to the Commons Health Select Committee from health authorities confirms that implementation of NICE guidance has meant a new phenomenon of 'postcode' cuts in other services in order to find funds for national standards.

Table 3: NICE Guidance 1999–2002, cost-per-QALY-gained, and the estimated cost impact of health technologies on the NHS

Topic	Recommendation	Incremental cost per QALY (if known):	Funding implications for NHS p.a.
Zanamivir in managing influenza	**No...** not recommended for 1999–2000 **...then Yes, but...** recommended for 2000–1 for some people when influenza levels are high	£9,300–£31,500	+ £2.3 m–11.7 m drug cost only
Removal of wisdom teeth	**No**		- Save up to £5 m
Coronary artery stents for ischaemic heart disease	**Yes** use routinely for patients with certain conditions		? 'Net impact difficult and potentially misleading'
Taxanes for ovarian cancer	**Yes, but...** use after surgery or for patients with recurrent ovarian cancer		+ £7 m net
Selection of replacement hips	**Yes, but...** recommended which types of artificial joint are likely to last longest		- Potential savings up to £8 m
Liquid based cytology for cervical screening	**Yes, but...** more evidence needed to justify nationwide introduction		= Possibly cost neutral
Taxanes for breast cancer	**Yes, but...** use for advanced breast cancer where chemotherapy has failed or is inappropriate		+ £16 m net
Proton pump inhibitors for dyspepsia	**Yes, but...** use only in specified cases		- Could save £40 m–50 m in drug costs
Hearing aid technology	**Yes, but...** insufficient evidence for digital hearing aids, but full range of analogue devices should be available		= Cost neutral
Rosiglitazone for type 2 diabetes mellitus	**Yes, but...** use for patients with inadequate blood glucose control on other medicines		+ Gross £14.5 m
Inhaler systems for under 5s with asthma	**Yes, but...** recommended where other treatments do not work		= Cost neutral if guidelines followed
Implantable cardioverter defibrillators (ICDs) for arryhthmias	**Yes, but...** recommended to prevent more serious problems in specific patient groups		+ £25 m–30 m net
Glycoprotein IIb/IIIa inhibitors for acute coronary syndromes	**Yes, but...** recommended for patients in specific circumstances		+ £30m–31 m net
Methylphenidate for attention deficit hyperactivity disorder (ADHD) in childhood	**Yes, but...** recommended as part of comprehensive programme for children with severe problems	£10,000–£15,000	+ £7 m upper limit
Tribavirin and interferon alpha for hepatitis C	**Yes, but...** recommended for patients with moderate to severe disease, depending on experience with other treatments	£3,000–£7,000 (first 6 months' treatment); £5,000–£36,000 second 6 months	+ £55 m spread over three years

Table 3: *contd.*

Topic	Recommendation	Incremental cost per QALY (if known):	Funding implications for NHS
Laparoscopic surgery for colorectal cancer	**No** Not recommended except in clinical trials		- Possible unquantified cost savings
Autologous cartilage transplantation for defects in knee joints	**No** Not recommended except in clinical trials		+ £3.6 m–6.9 m per year as second line treatment
Donepezil, rivastigmine, and galantamine for Alzheimer's disease	**Yes, but...** recommended as one component for managing mild and moderate Alzheimer's disease depending on circumstances	Estimate: £0–£30,000	+ £42 m per year
Laparoscopic surgery for inguinal hernias	**Yes, but...** recommended only for some kinds of hernia, restricted to appropriately trained teams	£50,000	? 'Budget impact . . . uncertain'
Riluzole for motor neurone disease (MND)	**Yes, but...** recommended for treatment of patients with one form of MND	£34,000–£43,000	+ £5 m net
Orlistat for obesity in adults	**Yes, but...** use for people already losing weight and restrict to adults who show specified improvements	£20 000–£30,000	+ £10 m net
Pioglitazone for type 2 diabetes mellitus	**Yes, but...** recommended as possible alternative to Rosiglitazone (see above)		- Eventual cost savings of £12 m per year
Topotecan for advanced ovarian cancer	**Yes, but...** recommended for specified cases		+ £7 m
Gemcitabine for pancreatic cancer	**Yes, but...** recommended for specified cases		+ £816,000 –£3 m
Wound care	**Yes, but...** recommended which dressings and techniques are most likely to reduce pain and be more acceptable to patients.		? 'difficult to estimate'
Cox II selective inhibitors of osteoarthritis and rheumatoid arthritis	**No** can be used when 'clearly indicated', after careful consideration of the risks and benefits		+ £25 m
Temozolomide for recurrent malignant glioma (brain cancer)	**Yes, but...** Use for some patients who have failed first-line chemotherapy		+ £1 m
Fludarabine for B-cell chronic lymphocytic laukaemia	**Yes, but...** use where chemotherapy has failed		= Not expected to result in a net increase
Docetaxel, Paclitaxel, Gemcitabine and Vinorelbine for non-small cell lung cancer	**Yes, but...** use for advanced cancers in specified situations		+ £3.8 to £15.3 m net
Sibutramine for obesity in adults	**Yes, but...** should be considered only for people meeting specified criteria.	£15,000–£30,000	+ £19.2 m net by Year 3

Source: For guidance issued from the inception of NICE to March 2001, this table has been adapted from Raftery (2001), Tables 1 and 2 (http://www.bmj.com/cgi/content/full/323/7324/1300/T1 and http://www.bmj.com/cgi/content/full/323/7324/1300/T2), with updates from March 2001–January 2002 from the published Guidance available on NICE's web page (www.nice.org/).

The judgement, and influence, of individual doctors remains the key determinant of patients' access to treatment.

Tackling the 'big killers'

Outside the NICE appraisal system, the Government's other explicit approach towards priority-setting has been its decision to make the 'big killers' of cancer and heart disease the subject of many of its targets and directives. While this is well intentioned, it risks priority being diverted away from non-targeted areas that may nevertheless represent good value for money. Priorities relating to particular conditions are driven by 'the size of the problem' – a needs-based, epidemiological approach.[25] However, this does not take account of the degree to which those conditions are amenable to change, nor the effectiveness or costs of interventions with which to effect that change. As a result, whether these are the 'right' priorities – and what the opportunity cost is of focusing on them instead of other services, which have to be set aside as a result – remains unknown. Progress towards a 'whole systems' approach to rationing and priority-setting is still lacking.

Aside from the 'big killers', priority-setting in the NHS remains largely a local issue. Labour has made little impact on the processes by which decisions are made about what services the NHS will *not* fund in a particular locality. Thus, primary care trusts are implementing the Government's 'must-dos', and, as a consequence, there is no consistency about what they choose not to pay for. A resolution about whether or not this is how politicians and the public want the NHS to be managed is still a long way off.

Conclusions

Rationing decisions and trade-offs occur at *every* level of decision-making in the NHS. The decision about how much of taxpayers' monies are to be devoted to the NHS (as opposed to defence, education and so on) is a rationing decision. Once that budget is determined, more can be allocated to one part of the health system only by allocating less to another; and within that, more can be spent on some kinds of services or conditions only by sacrificing other types of services or conditions.

A lack of progress

The first five years of Labour Government have done little to make these rationing processes more explicit than they were before. While the total amount of money given to the NHS is a political matter, which is frequently the subject of public debate, before being decided by the Chancellor of the Exchequer, the allocation of resources *between* services remains largely implicit – apart from imperatives created by national-level clinical priorities, targets and directives, including those resulting from NICE guidance.

Implicit rationing processes

For patients on NHS waiting lists, there remains no coherent system for setting priorities according to the urgency of their need. The judgement, and influence, of individual doctors remains the key determinant of patients' access to treatment. This has allowed the perverse situation where patients with relatively low clinical priority sometimes get treated ahead of more severe cases who have waited less – so health authorities can avoid missing waiting times targets. There is also no way of knowing from waiting list or times data whether access to surgery by people of similar need is similar across the country. Clearly, the manner in which decisions are made about how long people have to wait is not as fair as it could be.

In this context, the tendency of Government ministers to raise public expectations about the NHS is particularly damaging. By failing to engage honestly with the public about the need to make trade-offs in allocating health care resources to competing priorities, Labour has not only made itself a hostage to political fortune but has made the NHS more vulnerable to those who argue that it cannot survive in its present form.

The verdict

The establishment of NICE is a substantial achievement, helping to bring transparency and evidence-based consistency to decisions about new treatments. The impact of Government targets and priorities on other areas of treatment and care raise rationing dilemmas that remain obscure and are not being addressed. Local NHS managers and doctors are compelled to make trade-offs between different patients every day, with little support or guidance and barely any reference to the public.

5 Primary care

Key issues:

- Creating primary care groups and trusts
- Establishing personal medical services
- Developing NHS Direct and walk-in centres
- Improving quality in primary care

The inheritance

Controlling costs and quality through fundholding

The health policy pre-occupations of successive governments over the last 20 years have been consistent: containing costs and increasing efficiency, addressing variations in quality, and improving access and responsiveness to users. The Conservatives' reforms concentrated on controlling costs and quality through the introduction of the internal market. A central policy instrument was fundholding, which capitalised on general practitioners' intimate knowledge of local services and their financial entrepreneurialism. It gave practices who chose to join the scheme the ability to commission a wide range of services for their patients from hospital and community health services – sometimes gaining preferential treatment over the patients of non-fundholding practices.

Fundholding came to be seen as the spearhead of a 'primary care-led NHS'.[1] Although its champions claimed great benefits from the scheme, the evidence to support these claims was equivocal. Most fundholding practices had produced only modest service improvements, which were insufficient to justify their high cost.[2]

Ultimately, fundholding was unsuccessful in several respects

- It was bureaucratic, involving high transaction costs. It was perceived as unfair: fundholders generated inequities in access to care ('two-tierism').
- It was difficult to demonstrate that general practitioners were effective advocates in their patients' interests.
- Most importantly, the internal market failed to deliver the anticipated efficiency gains.[3]

Addressing GPs' concerns

The introduction of the internal market, and the imposition of a new national contract in 1990, caused considerable disquiet in the ranks of general practitioners. Many felt that the Government was ignoring their concerns and allowing their workload to rise inexorably. The British Medical Association was seeking to renegotiate the compulsory contractual requirement of 24-hour responsibility for care and to define more tightly the nature of 'core' general medical services (GMS).

Labour's pledge was
to remove the market
mechanism from the
NHS but retain the
split between
purchaser and
provider that was the
cornerstone of the
previous Government's
system.

Recruitment and retention of doctors was problematic, and there were many indications that a growing minority of GPs were seeking salaried or alternative employment options.[4] In response, ministers conducted a listening exercise among GPs across the country, to better understand their concerns and improve the conditions in which they were working. That exercise culminated in the publication of the White Paper *Choice and Opportunity,*[5] which promised to diversify the range of primary care services available to patients.

Opening up the primary care market

Before the 1997 election, the Conservative Government launched the Personal Medical Services (PMS) pilot schemes, marking the ending of GPs' monopoly of primary medical care, with new market entrants in the shape of NHS trusts and nurses.[6] With the development of alternative employment options to that of the independent contractor, the long-cherished national contract no longer to applied universally.

Labour inherited a divided medical profession. Having antagonised doctors in the early 1990s, successive Secretaries of State for Health had managed to placate them during the decade as fundholding became more popular and a series of improvements to their working lives were put in place. But inequities resulting from the Conservatives' handling of primary care remained.

The policy pledges

Abolishing GP fundholding

Labour's 1997 manifesto[7] promised that 'Primary care will play a lead role' in the party's rejuvenated NHS. While short on detail of how this would happen, the manifesto pledged to abolish GP fundholding. In its place, the manifesto said: 'GPs and nurses will take the lead in combining together locally to plan local health services more efficiently for all the patients in their area. This will enable all GPs in an area to bring their combined strength to bear upon individual hospitals to secure higher standards of patient provision. In making this change, we will build on the existing collaborative schemes which already serve 14 million people.' In addition, Labour pledged to remove the annual round of contracts between purchasers and providers, replacing them with longer-term 'agreements'.

Abolishing the internal market

The publication of Labour's 1998 White Paper *The New NHS: Modern, dependable*[8] formally announced the demise of GP fundholding. It underlined the role of the NHS in improving health, renewed an ideological commitment to equity in access and provision, and emphasised the need to ensure quality through clinical governance and accountability to local communities. Of fundamental importance was the move to loosen the restrictions of the NHS's old tripartite structure (of general practice, hospitals and community health services) by moving towards unified budgets and imposing a duty of partnership. Labour's pledge was to remove the market mechanism from the NHS but retain the split between purchaser and provider that was the cornerstone of the previous Government's system. The major structural change introduced to deliver these policy goals was the formation of primary care groups (PCGs) constituted from all the practices in a geographical area. PCGs were to be given responsibility for organising primary care services in their area, commissioning hospital services, improving the health of local people and ensuring their members provide high-quality care.

Developing new structures

More innovations were to follow during Labour's first term of office, specifically focusing on improved access to primary care. NHS Direct, for example, was conceived following a review of emergency services in 1997.[9] A nurse-led telephone helpline, it was designed to provide 'easier and faster advice and information for people about health, illness and the NHS so that they are better able to care for themselves and their families'.[10] More specific objectives for NHS Direct included the encouragement of self-care at home and reducing unnecessary use of other, more expensive, NHS services.

In addition, the Government developed the idea of NHS walk-in centres, most of them to be nurse-led. These were a specific response to the apparent success of instant access primary care facilities established by the private sector, notably on railway stations serving time-pressed commuters.

The NHS Plan, published in July 2000, heralded further organisational changes for primary care.[11] The Plan was supposed to represent a 'new deal' between the Government and the health sector (*see* box *below*). In return for substantial new funding, the Government sought to challenge some of the long-established foundations of the NHS and, in particular, to revisit the settlement between organised medicine and the state.

The NHS Plan – key points for primary care
- 500 one-stop health centres by 2004
- 3,000 surgeries upgraded by 2004
- 2,000 more GPs and 450 more registrars by 2004
- NHS Lift, a new private–public partnership to develop premises
- 1,000 specialist GPs
- Consultants delivering 4 million outpatient appointments in primary care
- Single-handed GPs to sign up to 'new contractual quality standards'

Published a year later, *Shifting the balance of power* provided the structural blueprint for implementing *The NHS Plan*.[12] The transfer of responsibilities to primary care trusts (PCTs) was further accelerated; their numbers doubled to 314 by April 2002. Twenty-eight strategic health authorities replaced 95 existing health authorities to develop strategy and performance manage PCTs and NHS trusts. Regional offices at the Department of Health were abolished and replaced by four regional directorates of health and social care, bringing the NHS one step closer to local government.

In 2001, Labour's manifesto commitments concerning primary care focused more on outcomes than reforms, for example, with the pledge that all patients will be able to see a GP within 48 hours by 2004.

The Government's actions

Reorganising primary care

PCGs began work in 1999, with three principal functions:[13]

- to improve the health of the population and address health inequalities
- to develop primary and community health services
- to commission a range of community and hospital services.

They brought together local providers of primary and community services under a board dominated by GPs, but also representing nurses, the local community, social services and the health authority. PCGs served populations averaging around 100,000 people and were expected to evolve over time into independent primary care trusts (PCTs). By April 2002, nearly all had made this transition. PCG/Ts were saddled with heavy expectations. In obvious respects they represented an evolutionary advance, giving all GPs the benefits of fundholding. But the creation of single budgets encompassing general medical services, prescribing, hospital and specialist care (rather than separating them, as previously) was revolutionary.

The duties of PCGs included clinical governance – using their new managerial structures to exert greater control over the quality of care provided by individual practices. Each PCG was required to ensure systems were put in place to monitor quality of care, to identify and tackle poor practice, to encourage the take-up of evidence-based procedures, and to ensure doctors underwent continuing professional development and education.

Though initially eclipsed by the creation of PCGs, the personal medical services (PMS) initiative was extended by Labour, as the pilot schemes proved unexpectedly popular. *The NHS Plan* enthusiastically supported the concept, and by April 2002 nearly one fifth of all GPs were working under PMS. Many of them are located in urban, more deprived areas, where the salaried option has been heavily taken up.

Improving access

NHS Direct was launched in three pilot sites in 1998, and rolled out rapidly thereafter. The service was available across the whole of England by the end of 2000 and now operates from 22 call centres, six of which serve the London area. A further three call centres are provided by NHS Direct Wales. A key development since the launch of NHS Direct is the adoption of a single, computerised decision-support system called CAS (clinical analysis software) in all call centres. This replaced the three different systems that were used by different centres until mid-2001 and will make it easier to ensure uniform standards of care across the country.

New roles for NHS Direct are under investigation – particularly in terms of integrating its triage function with access to out-of-hours medical care. There are 34 pilot sites for this development, of which 22 were launched in November 2001 and a further 12 started in March 2002. A typical pilot site exists in South London where access to the *Seldoc* out-of-hours GP co-operative is obtained through the South East London NHS Direct call centre. The centre employs 44 nurses and 26 call handlers, and receives approximately 500 calls per day.

Forty NHS walk-in centres have been launched since January 2000, of which nine are in London. They provide a range of high-quality minor ailment/treatment services to

A combination of unrealistic targets, a lack of resources, and the inadequacy of existing systems is seriously impeding PCTs' ability to generate the information needed to carry out their basic functions.

all patients, information about NHS, social services and other local statutory and voluntary services, and advice about self-care and about healthy lifestyles. The location and opening hours of walk-in centres are intended to promote convenient access for users. They are typically open from 7 am until 10 pm or 11 pm and while many are on sites adjacent to general hospitals, others are found in high streets and shopping centres – and one is in Manchester airport.

The Government has also begun to tackle the access problem implied in the dilapidated state of some GP surgeries, especially those in inner-city areas. Through the NHS LIFT initiative, public–private partnerships are being set up in a number of places to renovate outdated premises and build new surgeries where they are most needed (*see* Chapter 8 on the private sector).

The impact of policy

Building new organisations

Establishing an organisation was a key early preoccupation for PCGs, and they made sound progress in their early years. They have started to translate priorities into clear local health strategies, targets and action plans.

However, there remain concerns about whether primary care trusts (PCTs) will be able to realise their undoubted potential.[14,15] Not all PCG boards have functioned in a corporate manner, with general practitioners sometimes dominating board meetings at the expense of contributions from nurses, social services and lay members. There remain significant concerns about the degree to which practices are effectively engaged in the work of PCGs, and about the relative lack of progress in involving communities.

PCTs are beginning to get to grips with their responsibilities for managing budgets and influencing hospital services (*see* Figure 18), but many lack the necessary information and financial management capacity. A combination of unrealistic targets, a lack of resources, and the inadequacy of existing systems is seriously impeding PCTs' ability to generate the information needed to carry out their basic functions (*see* Figure 19).

Many PCTs have made considerable progress in developing minimum standards for general practice, agreeing plans for redistributing resources and improving services. Most have made a good start in establishing an infrastructure for clinical governance and initiating a range of activities involving practices and other staff.

In contrast, many have been hard-pressed to support the commissioning of hospital services or health improvement among their local population. And, although most have begun to develop closer links with social services departments, relationships with the wider local authority, such as housing or environmental health departments, are limited at this stage.

In summary, PCTs as organisations are developing at different speeds. They have made progress in developing and integrating primary and community care, but their commissioning and health improvement functions are, as yet, limited. There is a danger that national policy imperatives, central directives and guidance will stifle the development of local policies addressing local needs.

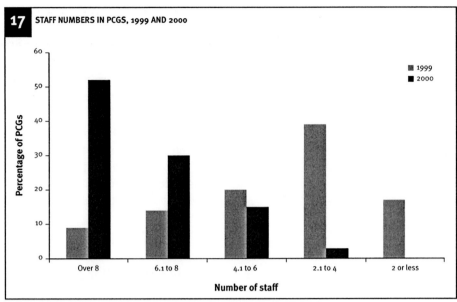

Source: National Tracker Survey of PCGs and PCTs. NPCRDC/King's Fund: 2000/2001

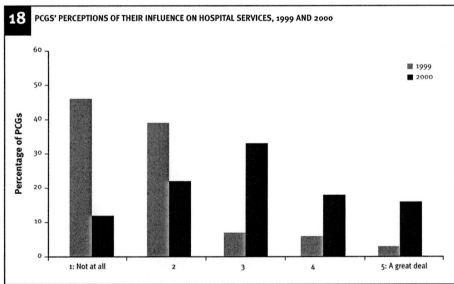

Source: National Tracker Survey of PCGs and PCTs. NPCRDC/King's Fund: 2000/2001

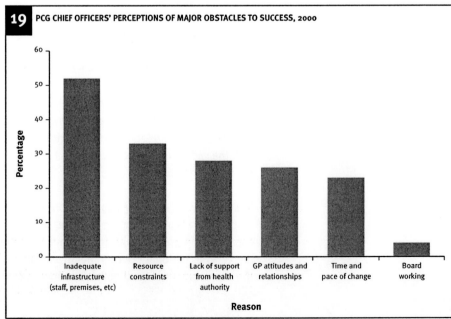

Source: National Tracker Survey of PCGs and PCTs. NPCRDC/King's Fund: 2000/2001

Clinical governance presents particular challenges for PCTs. They need to stimulate a major cultural change, encouraging professionals to see themselves as collectively accountable for the effectiveness of their colleagues' work.

Developing personal medical services

Personal medical services (PMS) pilots have proved to be a popular innovation. For the GPs involved in them, some of the financial risks and bureaucratic burdens of running a practice are reduced. Salaried GPs appear to be happier with their income and hours of work than GMS doctors on traditional contracts.[16]

It is hard to know how much service development can properly be attributed to PMS. First-wave pilots received an average of £62,900 extra on entering PMS, but there is, as yet, little evidence that they are delivering more improvements in patient care than GMS practices.[17]

PMS provides entrepreneurs with some of the independence previously enjoyed by fundholders, and its success partly reflects its appeal to practices disaffected with the current reforms. Paradoxically, some practices see PMS as a way of defining their own priorities and insulating themselves from the intrusions of PCTs. Nevertheless PMS, by putting responsibility for GPs' contracts in the hands of primary care trusts, provides them with crucial leverage over members with local, rather than national, contracts.

Implementing clinical governance

Clinical governance presents particular challenges for PCTs. They need to stimulate a major cultural change, encouraging professionals to see themselves as collectively accountable for the effectiveness of their colleagues' work.

Individual PCGs and PCTs have spent widely differing amounts on clinical governance. This, in turn, has led to variable levels of local support in the form of new staff.[18] Many clinical governance leads are scrambling up steep learning curves and only now are beginning to understand the complexity of their jobs. In over three-quarters of PCTs, each practice has appointed its own clinical governance lead. However, levels of support from other agencies, such as public health departments, academic bodies or education providers, vary considerably.[19]

The management of poor performance presents PCTs with another difficulty. Whereas previously patients' complaints, colleagues' expressed concerns and financial audit visits by the health authority used to be the main means of detection, PCTs are now responsible for setting up labour-intensive appraisal procedures.[20]

The emphasis so far has been on setting the right cultural tone, as much as on concrete achievements. In the wake of the murder conviction of GP Harold Shipman, which raised public fears about the safety of general practice, this has not been easy. PCTs are trying both to adopt a non-threatening, developmental approach to clinical governance and to set up new local monitoring mechanisms.[21] Yet the threats this appears to pose, both to independent contractor status and professional self-regulation, have increased doctors' feelings of beleaguerment.

Expanding the role of primary care

General practitioners were sceptical of claims that NHS Direct would reduce their workloads. Evaluation confirmed that, while the new service may have helped contain some GPs' workloads out-of-hours, it has had little impact on other emergency services.[22] It has proved to be popular with users, though the extent to which it benefits, for example, older people or minority ethnic populations remains contested.

Walk-in centres vary in the number and grades of nurses they employ in their level of provision of GP services and in the exact range of services they offer. [23] A recent study of walk-in centres [24] found the number of people attending them varied between 30 to 120 per day, with an average of 82 attendees. The average consultation length was 14 minutes, which is significantly longer than a general practice consultation. The most common presenting complaints were viral illnesses, unprotected sexual intercourse (to obtain emergency contraception), minor injuries, and dressings. Seventy-eight percent of consultations were managed entirely at the walk-in centres, without referral to any other health care provider.

NHS Direct and walk-in centres clearly illustrate the differences that diverse priority groups of people attach to access. The apparent popularity of these services with users contrasts with their reluctant acceptance by many health professionals. Concerns over their cost effectiveness remain but, both within and out of hours, numerous nurse-led providers – rather than the GP as the single gatekeeper – will increasingly form the first point of contact with NHS primary care services.

The Government's promised expansion in hospital beds and consultant numbers, with consequent reductions in waiting times, should ease the burden on primary care. Its plans to increase the number of GPs, however, are disappointing. An increase of 2,000 GPs represents only a modest increase in long-term trends. Even allowing for investment in other community-based services, GPs will not easily be able to improve access to their services or extend consultation lengths without a major expansion in their number.

Under *The NHS Plan*, patients who currently go to hospital will be able to have tests and treatment in one of 500 new primary care centres. Consultants who previously worked only in hospitals will be seeing outpatients in these new units, while 'GPs with special interests' will be taking referrals from their colleagues in fields such as ophthalmology, orthopaedics and dermatology. How these innovations will work in practice remains unclear.

Delegating power to the front line

Labour has repeatedly been criticised for its centralising tendencies at the expense of local experimentation. In *The NHS Plan*, trusts were promised considerable freedom from central supervision, and interference subject to satisfactory performance ('earned autonomy'). To monitor this, new accountability structures were created – many of them applying themselves to primary care organisations for the first time. The Modernisation Agency and numerous task forces are overseeing implementation of the Plan, and the capacity of the Commission for Health Improvement (CHI) has been extended. Though couched in a vocabulary suggesting local discretion, *The NHS Plan* thus tightens central control by limiting how trusts can use their new freedoms.[25] Whatever the Government's intentions, health professionals and managers fear they will be operating within an environment that is increasingly dominated by pre-determined clinical frameworks and an enhanced performance management system.

In April 2002, primary care trusts became the lead organisation for assessing needs, planning and securing all health services and improving health. Since 1 April 2002,

After nearly a decade
of rhetoric in support
of the 'primary care-
led NHS', there is little
evidence of a shift in
the balance of NHS
expenditure. In
absolute terms, it is
the acute sector that
continues to attract
most new money.

they are supposed to have been in control of three-quarters of NHS spending. There is plenty of evidence that PCTs vary greatly in the extent to which they are prepared for their new responsibilities. Many will be hindered in their new roles by inexperienced managers, unproven processes and fledgling support systems. Risk areas include corporate governance, information management, partnerships and commissioning, control of prescribing costs and personal medical services arrangements.[26] The Government is supposed to be giving power to the front line but at the same time has shown little enthusiasm for abandoning the range of targets that PCTs must meet.

Conclusions

The out-going Conservative Government presented the new Labour administration with many of the tools it has wielded in its quest for modernisation. The internal market has been adapted gradually within a framework of mandatory collective funding. In other respects, this Government has proved unexpectedly radical. Few people working in the NHS anticipated the series of initiatives designed to change the nature of first contact and to free up access to health care, which may fundamentally change the face of primary care in the long term.

Over the last five years, the NHS has undergone substantial organisational change, nowhere more than in primary care. Yet primary care is also notoriously resistant to change imposed externally. The long-term effects of Labour's reforms are, therefore, hard to predict, and there are still some areas of uncertainty about the extent to which Government policies are being implemented locally. It is still unclear how far primary care organisations will be able to substitute primary for hospital services, to improve health, and to overcome the centrifugal tendencies of many of their members.

A primary care-led NHS

After nearly a decade of rhetoric in support of the 'primary care-led NHS', there is little evidence of a shift in the balance of NHS expenditure.[27] In absolute terms, it is the acute sector that continues to attract most new money. In many areas, PCG mergers give PCTs the aura and scale of the health authorities they replaced. Yet it is unclear whether they will have the critical mass they need to lever resources from hospitals into community-based services.

There remains uncertainty about the capacity of these organisations to shape secondary and specialist care. They are unsure about what is best commissioned at what level. Responsibility for commissioning highly specialised, tertiary services is vested with groups of PCTs but exactly how this will work is still unclear. Giving PCTs the responsibility of commissioning hospital services locally – if it is to have any meaning – must amount to more than the 'freedom' to implement detailed Department of Health directives.

Primary care trusts need time to articulate a vision of how commissioning can make a difference to health care. They need a greater input of financial, physical and human resources including management support and information. At current capacity, it is difficult to see these new organisations effecting significant reconfigurations of secondary care.

Today, primary care trusts are bowing under the weight of the Government's good intentions.

Improving people's health

If primary care organisations are to drive forward public health goals, they need to reinforce the culture of support for 'upstream' solutions. They are already investing in services that will improve access and reduce variations in quality of care. And there are signs that these new organisations may yet make something of their health improvement role, particularly in Health Action Zones.[28] Health Improvement and Modernisation Programme (HIMP) sub-groups are beginning to invest in health-promoting initiatives beyond the NHS that address social determinants of health. They are predominately led by GPs than by any other health professional.

There have always been plenty of GPs who understand the central role of primary care in addressing health inequalities.[29] But others are less supportive of Labour's elevation of social exclusion to the centre of health policy. They view it as fostering a dependency relationship between the state and recipients of welfare benefits. Many doctors eschew involvement in 'lifestyle modification'. They plead for a form of medical practice that treats illness rather than regulating behaviour, and puts the autonomy of the individual and the privacy of personal life before political objectives. Reactionary challenges to the 'tyranny of health' and withdrawal from a wider social role are powerfully appealing to a constituency under pressure.[30]

Understanding the 'forces of conservatism'

Doctors are easily portrayed as part of the problem as they grapple with their responsibilities for modernisation. Once more they have appeared to 'dig in' – to resist central control and to assert financial independence. Many have well-founded concerns. They fear that the emergence of many more salaried doctors on PMS contracts may create a new form of 'two-tierism', with less well-remunerated, peripatetic doctors providing more care in deprived areas.

The gap between doctors who are PCT committee members and those who are not, in terms of their grasp of the modernisation agenda, is large. The latter see PCTs as adding to their workload. They do not want to take further responsibility for the rationing of health services implied in PCTs' commissioning role. Many GPs show little enthusiasm for the opportunities these reforms undoubtedly offer. Much hinges on the outcome of new contract negotiations.

Under Labour, primary care is effectively being collectivised into locally managed units responsible for managing the care of their populations. The GP surgery will increasingly become the service outlet for larger primary care organisations. Some 'corner shops' may disappear. But practices are likely to remain the basic building block of the NHS for the time being. And – as more and more practices take on new PMS contracts – local enterprise, rather than central diktat, could still be deployed to deliver the sustained improvements to the NHS that patients increasingly demand.

Today, primary care trusts are bowing under the weight of the Government's good intentions. They are struggling under a weight of unrealistic expectations generated by the Government's performance anxiety. Fears that PCTs may 'fail' to deliver *The NHS Plan* may, ironically, bring the health service full circle. The emergence of 'foundation' PCTs, and of practice-based budgets, could bring many elements of the internal market back to the NHS. PCTs need more time to deliver Labour's ten-year project. They are unlikely to get it.

The verdict

Ambitious reforms of primary care have removed many of the worst features of fundholding and appear to command widespread support. But the Government is pushing an under-resourced sector to do too much too quickly. Primary care trusts need more time and resources to make the changes that are expected of them.

6 Workforce

Key issues:

- Tackling the shortage of nurses, doctors and therapists in the NHS
- Improving the working lives of NHS staff
- Changing the NHS pay system
- Improving workforce planning in the health service

The inheritance

Workforce issues at the margins

When the Labour Government came to power in 1997, workforce issues were not squarely on the political agenda. The Conservatives had issued a number of initiatives, for example Project 2000, which reformed pre-registration training for nurses, but they lacked a cohesive policy around the NHS workforce. Workforce issues were often marginal to discussions around health policy and organisation.[1,2] Central workforce planning was all but non-existent, and planning within and between professions was fragmented. Only medicine, which for each professional group had been strictly centralised since the 1940s, remained centrally planned. Training budgets were kept rigidly separate. Local Education and Training Consortia (ETC) were established in 1996 to plan and commission non-medical education and training places but had little time to develop any influence before Labour came to power. Consequently, identifying the future workforce that would be needed – both in terms of numbers and composition – and taking action to secure it, had not been seriously attempted.

In the latter half of the Conservatives' 18-year term, recruitment and retention problems in the three major health professions – nursing and midwifery, medicine and the allied health professions – became more acute. What Labour inherited in each of these professions is outlined below.

Nurses and midwives

Pre-registration training places for nursing and midwifery were severely cut under the Conservatives in the 1980s to mid-1990s. By the end of the 1990s, this policy was significantly affecting the numbers of people qualifying and registering with the nursing and midwifery professional body, the UK Central Council for Nursing, Midwifery and Health Visiting (UKCC), and the number available for work in the NHS.[3] Figure 20 shows changes in the overall number of registrants with the UKCC from 1990 to 2001. Statistics up to 2001 are included because the Conservatives' policies continued to have an impact on the number of qualifying nurses for several years after Labour came into power. The same applies to figures provided for doctors and allied health professions.

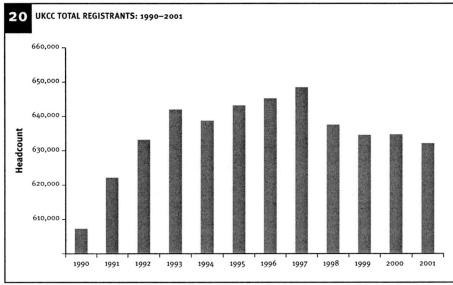

Source: UKCC Annual Statistics (Volume 1) 2000; Press release. 3 May 2001

Figure 20 shows that the overall number of registrants increased by almost 30,000 between 1990 and 2001, reaching a peak in 1997 and falling again thereafter. Since 1997, the number of people leaving the register has exceeded the number joining. In 1997/98, for example, 16,392 nurses and midwives joined the register while 27,173 left,[4] due, in part, to the earlier reduction in the number of pre-registration training places, which fell by 26 per cent between 1989/90 and 1994/95.[5] This fall may also be due to increasing numbers of nurses retiring, changes in post-registration education and training, and overseas nurses and midwives allowing their membership to lapse.

Doctors

The number of medical school places rose slightly during the mid- to late-1990s from 3,778 in 1994/95 to 3,804 by 1998/99. Figure 21 shows changes in the number of doctors registered with the General Medical Council since 1990.

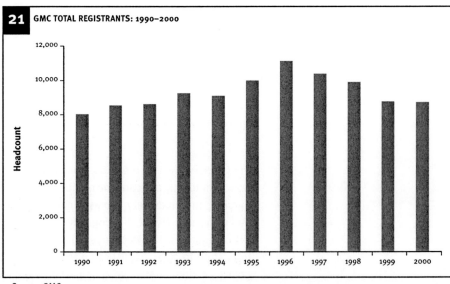

Source: GMC

This figure shows that the overall number of registrants increased between 1990 and 2000. However, it does not show the decline in the number of doctors becoming GPs during the same period.

Though recruitment and retention problems were widespread among the health professions during the Conservatives' successive terms in office there was a surprising lack of initiatives to address them.

Allied health professionals

The Council for the Professions Supplementary to Medicine (CPSM – due to become the new Health Professions Council) holds a register of state-registered allied health professionals, such as radiographers and physiotherapists. Figure 22 shows changes in the number of allied health professionals registered with the CPSM.

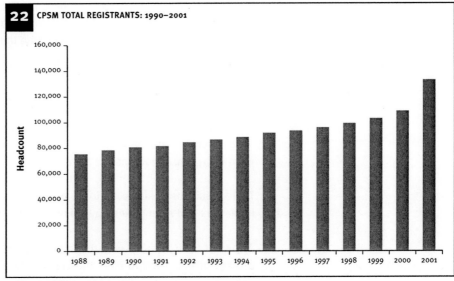

22 CPSM TOTAL REGISTRANTS: 1990–2001

Source: CPSM

The numbers of allied health professionals registered with the CPSM has steadily increased over the last 13 years to almost 133,400 by mid-2001. The sharp increase between 2000 and 2001 is probably due to three new professional groups – speech and language therapists, clinical scientists, and paramedics – becoming incorporated into the CPSM register.

Though recruitment and retention problems were widespread across the health professions during the Conservatives' successive terms in office there was a surprising lack of initiatives to address them – leaving the new Labour Government with a significant challenge. Therefore the primary focus of Labour's workforce agenda was addressing these recruitment and retention problems among clinical staff.

The policy pledges

Labour came to power on a manifesto that placed health fifth on its list of ten priorities. The manifesto did not contain any explicit pledges to or about the NHS workforce except for an indirect reference to spending extra money on patients and not bureaucracy (the usual euphemism for managers).

After taking office, Labour was quick to publish its plans for modernising the NHS.[6] In 1998, the Government published *Working Together: Securing a quality workforce for the NHS*[7] – an overview of Labour's strategic direction for addressing human resource (HR) issues in the health service. *Working Together* was a welcome first step towards putting HR issues on the agenda of trust chief executives and boards. The strategy involved building and supporting a quality workforce, providing a good working life for staff, and ensuring sufficient management capacity to oversee these objectives. It set target dates for meeting certain aspects of the policy. By April 2000, for example, HR directors would have to have in place training and development plans for the majority of health professional staff. More detailed plans for implementing key aspects of the policy overview were promised.

In *Improving Working Lives*, Labour made a commitment to make the working lives of NHS staff better suited to their needs.

The remaining workforce policy initiatives from Labour can be grouped under four broad promises: pay, working lives, workforce planning and staff numbers.

Pay

One of the key factors that influence a decision to leave a post is pay.[8] In 1999, the Government set out its plans for changing the NHS pay system.[9] It promised to develop a pay structure for the NHS workforce that would 'reward the actual responsibilities that staff take on rather than the job title they work under'.

The new pay system would be based on:

- new ways of working and breaking down traditional barriers
- principles of equal value and career progression through competence and satisfactory performance
- national core conditions but 'considerable' local flexibility.

There would be a single national negotiating council, a national job evaluation framework and a simplified pay spine with thresholds for key career stages.

As part of plans to assist with recruitment and retention, the Government promised a range of initiatives to ease the costs of living and accommodation, such as a national housing co-ordinator to assess accommodation problems and 2,000 more units for nurse accommodation in London by 2003.[10]

Working lives

In *Improving Working Lives*, Labour made a commitment to make the working lives of NHS staff better suited to their needs through family friendly working opportunities, support with childcare, tackling harassment, violence and discrimination, and giving staff more control over their working environments. There would be a national campaign to promote family friendly and flexible working practices; regional taskforces would be set up to share good practice; and targets would be agreed and set for all NHS employers.[11,12]

Workforce planning

In March 1999, widespread concern about current arrangements for workforce planning, education and training led the House of Commons Health Select Committee to recommend a major review of workforce planning in the NHS.[13] The Government accepted the findings of this report, which recognised many of the problems were longstanding and the result of failure by previous governments to tackle them.[14] In a detailed response to the report – the consultation document *A Health Service of all the Talents: Developing the NHS workforce* [15] – the Department of Health proposed new systems for workforce planning to include:

- merging education and training levies
- encouraging experimentation with skill-mix changes and new types of working within and between the professions
- establishing clearer lines of responsibility and accountability for workforce planning at local, regional and national level: in particular, new Workforce Development Confederations would replace the ETC. They would have a wider remit than the ETC, bringing together all employers of health care staff at a regional level to plan current and future staffing requirements, commission training

places, evaluate the existing mix of health professions and experiment with alternatives
- exploring multi-professional education and training opportunities.

The review acknowledged there were staff shortages within the service but suggested any attempts to increase staff numbers would have to be matched by thinking around how staff might work differently to deliver services: 'looking at the workforce in a different way, as teams of people rather than as different professional tribes.'[16]

Staff numbers

The NHS Plan[17] set out targets for increasing the numbers of key NHS staff:
Between 2000 and 2004, the Government promised to recruit:

- 20,000 more nurses
- 7,500 more consultants
- 2,000 more GPs
- 6,500 more therapists.

In addition, the Plan stated that annually, by 2004, there would be:

- 4,450 new training places for therapists and 'other key professional staff'
- 5,500 new nurse training places
- 450 new general practice training posts
- 1,000 specialist registrar posts.

By 2005, the Government pledged to increase medical school places by up to 1,000.

In addition to the policies mentioned above under the four broad promises, rafts of other workforce documents were issued by Labour (*see* box *below*).

Key workforce initiatives under Labour

1998 *Working Together: Securing a quality workforce for the NHS*
1999 *Agenda for Change: Modernising the NHS pay system*
1999 *Making a Difference: Strengthening the nursing, midwifery and health visiting contribution to health and healthcare*
1999 *Making a Difference to Nursing and Midwifery Pre-registration Education*
1999 *Improving Working Lives in the NHS*
2000 *A Health Service of all the Talents: Developing the NHS workforce*
2000 *The NHS Plan: A plan for investment. A plan for reform*
2000 *Improving Working Lives Standard*
2000 *Meeting the Challenge: A strategy for the allied health professions*
2001 *Modernising Regulation in the Health Professions*

The Government's actions

Labour's promises were wide-ranging and ambitious. Progress on implementing them is detailed below.

Changing pay structures

The Government first set out its intention to change pay structures for the health professions in 1999. It reiterated this commitment in *The NHS Plan*. A further document reporting progress and setting out a timetable for implementing the new pay structures has long been promised but has not, as yet, been published.

During Labour's first five years, the health professions experienced year on year pay increases that barely kept up with inflation. In the latest round, however, which will take effect from 1 April 2002, nurses and midwives and doctors were awarded a 3.6 percent increase on their basic pay. Newly qualified physiotherapists, occupational therapists and radiographers would benefit from a 7.5 percent increase. In the previous round, doctors were awarded a 3.9 percent rise while nurses and midwives received a 3.7 percent increase. Senior nurses, on whom the Government depended to implement key aspects of *The NHS Plan*, were awarded a 5 percent rise. As a result, real pay has risen. Labour also ended the Conservatives' practice of staging pay increases – but only after its first pay settlement for nurses was staged, with the full rise not provided until December: eight months into the financial year.

In addition to basic pay award increases, a new type of 'bonus' award has been introduced in the form of 'golden hellos' and 'goodbyes' for doctors and nurses. Newly qualified GPs will receive a 'golden hello' of £5,000, with an extra £5,000 if they begin work in a deprived area. Family doctors who wait until they are 65 to retire will receive a £10,000 'golden goodbye'. Nurses, midwives and therapists who take a return to practice course will receive £1,000.[18]

To assist with pay and costs of living, Labour increased the London allowance for nurses by 3.7 percent in 2001, and boosted the inner-city and outer-city living allowances. A national housing co-ordinator was appointed in 2000 and a new scheme to help nurses and other public sector workers buy their first home was announced in September 2001.[19]

Working lives – setting up targets

The *Improving Working Lives Standard*,[20] which sets out the various targets all NHS employers are expected to meet, was issued in 2000.

Under the terms of the standard, by 2003, employers must prove that they:

- are committed to staff training and development
- are tackling harassment and discrimination
- are acting on the Government's zero-tolerance policy on violence against staff
- have a workforce that is representative of the local community
- and offer flexible and family-friendly working opportunities.

Workforce Development Confederations

The 24 Workforce Development Confederations (WDCs), promised in 2000, went live in April 2001. Education and training levies were merged and now fall under the

Although pay levels have been increased substantially, particularly by the last two Review Body settlements, a large proportion of these increases compensate for a period of pay restraint during the 1990s.

remit of the WDCs. From April 2002, the WDCs will be able to take on responsibility for the Medical and Dental Education Levy, unifying the budgets for medical and non-medical training – this means that almost all financial support for training is in one pot. Clearer lines of accountability for workforce planning at local, regional and national level have now been established.

Following the launch of *The NHS Plan*, a national Workforce Taskforce was set up to encourage and assess local progress towards key targets set down in the Plan. One of those targets included investigating ways staff might work differently. The Changing Workforce Programme was subsequently set up to experiment with this, for example, by moving a task up or down a traditional uni-disciplinary ladder. Examples include allowing specialist registrars to perform tasks previously carried out only by consultants, or expanding the number of tasks nurses can take on.

Increasing staff numbers

Training places for nurses and midwives, doctors and allied health professions have been increased, in line with *NHS Plan* targets, and will continue to increase year on year until 2004.

Recruitment campaigns have been run annually since 1999 to entice people into the NHS workforce. In the last couple of years the Government has also run 'returners' campaigns to attract former staff back to the NHS. Considerable effort has also been made to entice overseas-trained nurses and doctors to the NHS. A specific arrangement has been made with Spain to provide the NHS with nurses.

The impact of policy

Pay – a mixed reception

The Government's proposals to change the pay structure for the health professions were published in 1998. What progress has been made on developing this structure and agreeing a timetable for its implementation has yet to be made public.

Although pay levels have been increased substantially, particularly by the last two Review Body settlements, a large proportion of these increases compensate for a period of pay restraint during the 1990s. Furthermore, concerns remain about the level of pay for some professions. For example, pay for nurses, midwives and the allied health professions still lags behind that of other public sector workers.[*]

Labour's golden 'hellos' and 'goodbyes' for GPs and nurses received a mixed reception. Some said they would make a real difference;[21] others dubbed them 'handcuffs'.[22] What impact they have had is not yet clear: take-up figures for these financial incentives are not yet available.

Cost-of-living supplements and accommodation support have been welcomed but are still not considered sufficient to compensate for higher living costs – particularly in London and the south east of England. Transport costs for staff working in the capital remain a significant issue, especially considering other public sector workers, for example, officers in the Metropolitan Police, receive a travel subsidy.

---

[*] For example, a qualified nurse starts work on £15,445 and a physiotherapist on £15,920. A qualified teacher starts work on £16,038 or £17,001 (depending on their level of attainment) and an untrained policy officer starts work on £17,133.

The Government has made a concerted effort to improve the working lives of staff. However, many of these policies are taking a long time to translate into tangible support for staff on the ground.

Working lives – slow progress

The Government has made a concerted effort to improve the working lives of staff. However, many of these policies, for example, flexible and family-friendly working and assistance with child care arrangements, are taking a long time to translate into tangible support for staff on the ground.[23] Furthermore, 'worrying' proportions of staff are unaware of the opportunities available to them.[24] Moreover, many of the targets, for example for 100 trusts to have on-site nurseries by 2004, are modest.

Despite the Government's efforts to make working lives better in the NHS, morale amongst health service staff appears to be at a low ebb. According to a recent King's Fund study, there are three key reasons for low morale amongst NHS staff:

- a feeling that they are not valued, that their work is not appreciated
- a working environment that frustrates and constrains staff, for example because of shortages
- pay levels that do not appear to reflect their skills and commitment.[25]

NHS and other public sector workers have received mixed messages about how far their work is valued by government ministers. Some of the rhetoric, for example about the 'forces of conservatism' in the public sector, has been positively harmful to morale. While ministers frequently tell NHS staff they are valued in set-piece speeches, their actions can suggest a distrust of public sector workers. The Government's apparent enthusiasm for using private sector providers as an alternative to NHS staff has been particularly controversial.

In addition, the organisational turbulence and pursuit of targets that has characterised the health service over the past decade, including before Labour came to power, has taken the attention of senior NHS managers away from staffing matters. The result has been that staff and managers feel unsupported, and both perceive that their concerns about poor working conditions are not being tackled.

Workforce planning – a short-term focus?

The Workforce Development Confederations are young organisations and it is too early to evaluate their impact. They have spent much of their first year establishing themselves and developing their agendas. There has been little time to experiment. Certainly, their potential to tackle recruitment and retention problems, and to develop the future health care workforce, is great. But there are several obstacles they will need to overcome, including a lack of adequate and reliable workforce data, and the fact that NHS workforce issues are not yet high enough on many NHS employers' agendas.[26] They will also need support from the centre, and should not have to worry that their second-year budgets are under threat, as they currently are.

The Government's own efforts to improve workforce planning have focused largely on the clinical professions, especially doctors and nurses. The other professional groups which comprise the NHS workforce have received less attention. Despite the organisational change that has characterised the past five years in the NHS, for example, the management requirements of the NHS have received little attention from ministers. The result is that, in many areas, primary care groups and trusts have struggled to meet the demands expected of them without the management capacity to achieve them.[27]

Staff numbers – will they be enough?

The headline figures in *The NHS Plan* proposed for the expansion of NHS staff were encouraging at first but further analysis revealed several caveats.

- The numbers of nurses were headcount figures not whole-time equivalents (or WTEs). This potentially lowers the resulting contribution to the service because many health workers are on part-time contracts.
- 4,500 new consultants,[28] 1,100 extra GPs,[29] and a significant proportion of the nursing component were already due to join the workforce when *The NHS Plan* was drafted, for example, from earlier increases in training places.
- As it was clear that not all these posts could be filled by UK-trained health professionals, there would be a significant reliance on overseas recruitment to plug the gaps until more UK-trained graduates came online – accepting that they may not remain in the NHS indefinitely.

By December 2001, the Government claimed to be half way towards its target of 20,000 more nurses by 2004.[30] It is likely that that number will increase in the next year as some 29,000 overseas-trained nurses complete adaptation courses and become eligible to join the UKCC register and work in the NHS. But there are still worrying problems within nursing and midwifery.

- The nursing workforce is ageing, which means the number of nurses forecast to retire will double from 5,500 a year to more than 10,000 a year by 2005.[31]
- The number of overseas-trained nurses and midwives joining the register is set to exceed the number of UK-trained nurses and midwives, partly as a result of government recruitment drives to boost nursing numbers.
- The NHS is struggling to retain staff and plug the gaps that leavers create.

The most recent NHS vacancies survey found there were 9,000 nursing and midwifery vacancies at the end of March 2001 – 1,000 less than the previous year.[32] However, the survey only includes vacant posts that trusts have been actively trying to fill for three months. By counting an established post as vacant the moment it becomes unfilled, as well as counting posts that have been frozen, the Royal College of Nursing (RCN) estimates the real vacancy rate may be nearer to 22,000 WTE.[33] And even if the Government meets its ambitious targets, they may not be sufficient. The RCN claims that if retirement and other losses remain constant, the NHS will need to recruit more than 110,000 nurses by 2004 to plug the gaps.[34]

By September 2001, there were 25,690 consultants working in the NHS – an increase of 5.7 percent on the previous year. During the same period, there was a meagre 1.4 percent increase in the number of GPs, taking it to 30,685.[35] The latest NHS vacancies survey revealed there were 670 consultant post vacancies. A separate survey of general practitioner vacancy rates found 1,214 vacancies. That number, in particular, looks set to increase as significant numbers of Asian GPs recruited to plug gaps in the 1970s approach retirement in the next few years. In some health authorities, many of them in the most deprived areas of the country, this could mean a loss of one in four GPs.[36] The ability to fill these posts is compromised by the modest supply of newly qualified GPs – which hit an all time low in 1998 and has barely recovered since.[37]

Upstream, while the number of places available may be increasing, the number of applicants to medical school are falling. In 1994, the University and College Admissions Service (UCAS) received 11,671 applications to study medicine. By 1996,

Managers themselves have been largely peripheral to discussions around the NHS workforce, except in the negative sense of a promise to reduce bureaucracy and re-divert any savings into patient care.

UCAS received 12,025 applications, but by 1998 applications dropped to 11,807, and by 2000, applications had dropped further to 10,226.[38]

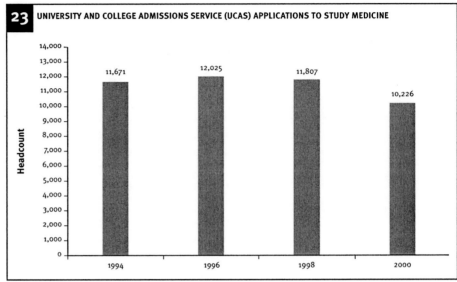

23 UNIVERSITY AND COLLEGE ADMISSIONS SERVICE (UCAS) APPLICATIONS TO STUDY MEDICINE

Source: UCAS

Faced with a supply problem of UK-trained doctors, the Government has turned to other countries to recruit staff. But, in recent years, the favourable trend in overseas-trained doctors joining the register has tapered off. In 1996, for example, 7,150 doctors from overseas joined the register, of whom 2,435 trained in the European Economic Area. By 2000, that number had decreased to 4,244 of whom 1,380 were EEA-trained. Should this trend continue, it could significantly affect the Government's plans to recruit overseas doctors to plug gaps in the NHS.[39]

By September 2001, the number of allied health professionals had increased by 4 percent over the previous 12 months, to a total of 51,320.[40] But at the same time, vacancy rates among the allied health professions have been increasing. In March 2001, there were 1,820 vacancies for qualified allied health professionals[41] – 300 more than at the same time the previous year.

Conclusions

A high-enough priority?

Many of Labour's initiatives for addressing NHS workforce issues have been appropriately targeted at the deficiencies noted by staff, such as improving pay and working lives. But many are yet to make a real difference for staff, who are often unaware of the opportunities available to them. Recruitment and retention problems persist. In many trusts, workforce issues are yet to become a priority, as they compete for attention with the myriad other targets their chief executives have to meet. Managers themselves have been largely peripheral to discussions around the NHS workforce, except in the negative sense of a promise to reduce bureaucracy and re-divert any savings into patient care. This is despite the fact that managers are responsible for overseeing implementation of the workforce and wider NHS modernisation agendas.

The strategic focus on improving working lives and pay suggests that Labour recognises the value of the health care workforce. However, the Government treads a precarious line between such support and blame, leaving NHS staff and managers unsure of where they stand. A recent example of this followed an Audit Commission report,[42] which showed that waiting times in A&E were higher than five years previously: when ministers became aware of the statistics, they were reported to have warned that NHS managers whose trusts continued to under-perform in this area would be replaced.

At a time of significant change in the NHS and great pressure to achieve the Government's modernisation targets, staff motivation is vital. The ambitious targets set in *The NHS Plan* will only be implemented by a sufficiently highly motivated workforce which feels enthusiasm for what ministers want to achieve. Many of the National Service Frameworks for specific patient groups, for example, require staff to undertake additional training, for which many are unable to get time away from their regular work because of staffing pressures. Low morale and staff shortages thus act in a vicious circle which the Government will have to break if its ambitions for the NHS are to be realised.

Short-term thinking

Labour's policies on the NHS workforce, although welcome, have a predominantly short-term focus, working to a politically expedient timetable. There remains an important policy debate about the wider vision for the NHS workforce, incorporating discussions around how – with a limited complement of staff – the workforce might be reconfigured to better meet patients' needs. Labour set the agenda for this discussion when it outlined its plans for modernising the career structure for nurses. Some models for reorganising the workforce have been suggested.[43,44] But there are still entrenched views on all sides, which inhibit open discussion of new models of working and experimentation. Equally, there must be a robust review of the evidence-base for alternative workforce models, which is currently limited and biased.[45]

Significant challenges ahead

Labour has acknowledged the problems facing the NHS workforce and developed a programme of work to address them. The programme is comprehensive, ambitious and timely, but there are still significant challenges. Recruitment and retention problems, for example, are acute, forcing many trusts to rely heavily on expensive agency and locum support. In general practice, the worst problems may be yet to come, as retirement levels among inner city GPs begin to rise over the next ten years. Unless issues such as these are resolved, the Government's modernisation agenda for the NHS will be compromised.

The verdict

Five years after Labour took power, the NHS remains desperately short of staff in many areas. Labour inherited many of these problems and is now making a committed effort to tackle the shortages the service faces. Early indications are that the Government has succeeded in increasing staff numbers in the NHS, but whether it will make a substantial impact in the longer term, against a background of ever-rising retirement levels in the service, is unclear. Labour has made a start in addressing longer-term issues, but, so far, little progress has been made. In particular, there has been no systematic attempt, as yet, to develop effective links between service redesign, changes in clinical technology, and the content of training and lifetime learning.

7 Quality assurance

Key issues:

- Creating systems for improving quality of care within the NHS
- Measuring the performance of NHS trusts
- Reforming professional self-regulation
- Managing poor performance by NHS staff

The inheritance

Public concern about the quality of care that they receive from the NHS has been rising in recent years. In an increasingly consumer-driven society, informed by media reports of the opportunities offered by modern treatment, expectations of what health care should be like have been rising. These expectations are not always met in people's experiences of the NHS, or, indeed, of private medical care. This, alongside growing evidence of variable standards of care, has made the quality agenda an unavoidable political issue.

Medical audit

In 1991, the mainstay of the quality agenda was medical audit, later broadened to clinical audit. The Government's role was to fund the process and to set out an organisational framework, leaving the rest of the system to the discretion of the medical profession.[1] The process was entirely confidential to the doctors involved.

In 1996, the Government acted to take greater control over audit activity. Health authorities were made responsible for audit monies and became subject to performance management by the NHS Executive for their use. They were expected to lead the development of a programme that linked to the implementation of national guidelines and involved a broader spectrum of health professionals, managers, researchers, purchasers and patients in increasingly wide-ranging audits and reviews.[2] This change in funding provided the first lever for ensuring more accountable national systems for improving quality. For the first time, those outside of medicine had a greater say in the agenda for clinical audit.

The years immediately preceding 1997 also saw numerous new policies emerge to promote the wider quality agenda set by the advent of evidence-based practice.[3,4,5] These included investment in research, and guidelines and outcome indicators, alongside a raft of advice and guidance to the service on how to develop and assure evidence-based approaches to quality health care. The Conservative Government invested in demonstration projects to lead the way in closing the gap.[6,7,8,9,10] They showed how complex the task of changing and improving clinical practice was, as well as helping to develop NHS staff with new skills as quality facilitators and quality project managers.[11]

From the first paragraph of Tony Blair's foreword to the Government's first White Paper on health, the emphasis was on delivering 'dependable, high-quality care'.

Performance measurement

Quantifying the performance of the NHS – primarily through performance indicators derived from routine data collection – has been common practice for many years. Previous Conservative administrations had developed performance indicators, mainly disseminated to the NHS as a comparative tool to prompt health authorities and trusts to improve their performance. While the internal market of the early 1990s assumed a greater role as a mechanism for improving performance, performance indicators continued to be produced for comparative purposes (not least to inform purchasers in the internal market). A key *composite* measure of efficiency – the purchaser efficiency index – was used not only to measure performance, but also as a basis for target setting for authorities. But this measure of efficiency led to perverse behaviour in the NHS.

The Conservative era provided Labour with a platform from which it could launch its more integrated approach to quality as well as giving many people in the NHS the practical experience necessary to turn new policy objectives into action.

The policy pledges

In its first two years of office, the Government's first White Paper [12] and subsequent policy documents laid out many aspirations, such as ensuring access to the same high level of care across the country. Only later did it turn its attention to more detailed plans that sought to ensure public protection from poor NHS performance and to put in place a systematic approach to spreading good practice across the service.

Like any government, Labour also had to develop policy in response to events – particularly past failures that had been subject to scrutiny or current failings that became the stuff of media sensation and political controversy. However, the Government launched a number of high-profile independent inquiries into the failings of the NHS. The inquiry into the scandal of children's deaths after cardiac surgery at Bristol Royal Infirmary was perhaps the most important, not just in terms of its scale, but in the scope of its recommendations.[13] Among the many other dissections of the past that occurred were the circumstances that allowed rogue individuals like the gynaecologist Rodney Ledward to continue unchecked,[14] or the collection of deceased children's organs without consent at Alder Hey Hospital in Liverpool,[15] as well as the murders of Harold Shipman.[16] These inquiries have provided the Government with a platform for more radical action to reform professional regulation,[17] develop more effective systems to regulate private health care,[18] and reform the legal and procedural systems for seeking consent.[19]

Grand blueprints: the New NHS

From the first paragraph of Tony Blair's foreword to the Government's first White Paper on health, the emphasis was on delivering 'dependable, high quality care'. New mechanisms were promised for assuring and improving quality. The White Paper promised that the new NHS 'will have quality at its heart'.[20] Labour offered no slick mantra for its definition of quality but it became clear that, at the heart of its approach, was the reduction of 'unacceptable' variation not only in the quality of care but in access to it.

To achieve this end, the 1997 White Paper promised new national standards and an organisation (the National Institute for Clinical Excellence) to take up the task of producing national guidelines for best practice based on evidence of clinical and cost-effectiveness. There would be a new system of clinical governance to ensure that standards of good practice were met and processes were in place in every trust to ensure continuous improvement. It promised a new statutory duty for quality on NHS trusts (until that point they were only duty-bound to keep their organisations financially solvent). It also proposed the establishment of another new organisation, the Commission for Health Improvement (CHI), whose main task would be to review clinical governance arrangements in each and every NHS organisation over a rolling five-year cycle. Where there was a justifiable cause for concern over a trust's performance CHI would also be able, under direction from the Secretary of State for Health, to undertake a rapid inspection and review of the organisation in question.

Six months later, in June 1998, the full blueprint arrived in the form of *A First Class Service: Quality in the new NHS*.[21] This covered five main themes:

- The promise of *national consistency* in the implementation of evidence-based practice and the introduction of new health care innovation.
- A new *accountability* for ensuring the local implementation of best practice.
- A commitment to a co-ordinated and systematic approach to undertaking audit, promoting clinical effectiveness, managing complaints, tackling risks and working for better quality information on clinical performance – in short a coherent system of *quality improvement and assurance*.
- New commitments concerning the *management of poor performance*. The blueprint proposed placing a responsibility for clinical governance on chief executives, requiring appraisal systems within trusts, establishing an inspectorate to visit trusts, and obliging all hospital doctors to take part in national audit. To this were added promises about the modernisation of professional self-regulation.
- An emphasis on *professional collaboration and teamwork*. It promised to put the experience of the patient at the centre of the quality improvement process.

Public protection

The next tranche of policy, emerging in 1999 and 2000, concentrated on the links that were needed to make this raft of policy objectives coherent. The focus here was on *public protection* from poor performance.

Leading the way were promises for a fundamental change in the relationship between patient, professional, manager and Government. For example, proposals were made to sweep away old rules governing the management of doctors. Trusts and health authorities, or primary care trusts in relation to GPs, were to have the authority to conduct annual appraisals with doctors; while doctors faced new obligations to take part in clinical audit and clinical governance and to undergo the appraisal.[22] Participation in appraisal, and the generation of comparative data, would then form part of the process for five-year revalidation by the General Medical Council – the doctors' professional regulatory body. In the case of possible poor performance, it promised that concerns would lead to doctors being referred to a new 'support and assessment' service.

Organisational learning

As well as developing policy that could address potential poor organisational performance, the Government promised to ensure that the whole NHS learnt from those parts of the service that got it right – to spread good practice more quickly and efficiently.

The most striking feature of Government action has been the establishment of new central bodies to take on distinctive tasks.

To make this happen, the Government has proposed a variety of methods over the past five years, from 'loose learning networks' such as the NHS Beacon scheme, to the imposition of new managerial teams on failing trusts through 'NHS franchising'.[23,24] The Government promised to provide the systems and organisations to help identify best practice and make it accessible to others.[25] It promised central support (through the Clinical Governance Support Team) to enable local organisations to develop good systems of clinical governance [26] as well as help in redesigning priority services so that they could reach national targets, through the National Patient Access Team.[27] Measures were also proposed to develop the sort of leadership that could enable NHS organisations to foster innovation and improvement.[28]

Another aspect of organisational learning focused on the need to learn from error. The foreword to the Chief Medical Officer's report on learning from adverse events pointed out that 'advances in knowledge and technology... have immeasurably increased the complexity of the health care system... and with that complexity comes an inevitable risk'. The report recommended the creation of a new national system for reporting and analysing adverse health care events.[29] The Government promised to take the necessary action.

Performance assessment

Labour's revamp of the Purchaser efficiency index and the plethora of performance indicators introduced over the previous decade was first detailed in a consultation document.[30] This proposed a set of performance 'domains' that reflected the key objectives of the NHS (efficiency, effectiveness, equity, etc), supported by a limited set of performance measures. Given the criticisms of the purchaser efficiency index, no aggregation of these measures was proposed; rather, the performance assessment framework (PAF) was to be viewed as a 'balanced scorecard', reflecting performance changes across all the objectives of the NHS for all NHS organisations.

Not only were these new sets of performance measures to be disseminated in the NHS, they were also to serve as the baseline information for reporting changes in performance of the NHS to the public.[31,32]

The Government's actions

The most striking feature of Government action has been the establishment of new central bodies to take on distinctive tasks. The new bodies and their roles in delivering this ambitious agenda fall into three categories:

- those attempting to have an impact on the performance of NHS organisations *and* clinical professionals, through setting national standards, building clinical governance and assessing performance
- those with a remit specifically to address the performance of NHS organisations
- those with a particular remit to assure the performance of individual clinical professionals – particularly through the reform of the existing mechanisms for professional regulation.

Setting national standards

The National Institute for Clinical Excellence (NICE) was set up on 1 April 1999. Its role was to provide patients, health professionals and the public with authoritative, robust and reliable guidance on current 'best practice'. NICE has two main outputs: national guidance on the clinical management of specific conditions; and recommendations over the funding of new medicines, medical devices, and diagnostic procedures, based on cost and clinical effectiveness information. NICE is discussed in greater detail in Chapter 4.

The Department of Health itself took on a major role in implementing the Government's promises of greater national consistency. It began to produce National Service Frameworks, designed to define service models from the perspective of the patient – irrespective of organisational boundaries. These frameworks came with performance milestones against which progress within an agreed timescale is measured, alongside information and organisational strategies to support implementation. They aim to raise the quality and decrease the variations in key services.

A framework for mental health was published in September 1999,[33] one for coronary heart disease in 2000,[34] and a *National Cancer Plan* in September 2000[35] – which itself built on the 1995 Calman/Hine report [36] (produced under the Conservative Government). Frameworks for services for older people and for diabetes were published in 2001.[37] For many of these topics, national directors, often dubbed 'tsars' have been appointed to promote improvements and monitor standards of care. The Department of Health anticipate one National Service Framework each year – the current programme gives a commitment to the development of frameworks for renal services, children's services and long-term conditions.[38]

Building clinical governance

Clinical governance is a framework for making all NHS staff accountable for quality improvement and safeguarding standards. The Department of Health defined clinical governance 'as a framework through which NHS organisations are accountable for continuously improving the quality of their services and safeguarding high standards of care by creating an environment in which excellence in clinical care will flourish'. [39]

The Government's first piece of legislation established a statutory duty of quality on NHS organisations: 'it is the duty of each Health Authority, Primary Care Trust and NHS Trust to put and keep in place arrangements for the purpose of monitoring and improving the quality of health care which it provides to individuals'.[40] It also put in place performance management structures to ensure action on clinical governance (including inspection by CHI) and placed trusts under an obligation to produce an annual clinical governance report.

The Government wove a clinical governance thread through policy developments across the board. Typical of this is the way clinical governance responsibilities have been enshrined in the organisational structure of new primary care trusts (PCTs). Government guidance guarantees clinical governance leads a place on the board and makes the extended reach of CHI into PCTs abundantly clear: 'the Commission will have a key role in the assurance that clinical governance is being implemented ... it will conduct a rolling programme of reviews visiting every PCT over a period of around 3–4 years'.[41]

The Commission started work on 1 April 2000. In 2001, it published clinical governance reviews on 70 trusts and the results of investigations into potential problems in service quality in another five. It has also conducted the first review of the implementation of national standards in cancer care and it will publish similar reviews for each National Service Framework.[42]

To cover the private sector, the Government established the National Care Standards Commission (NCSC).[43] From 1 April 2002, it will regulate social care and private and voluntary health care in England, including care homes, children's homes, private and voluntary hospitals and clinics, and nursing agencies. The NCSC aims to regulate and inspect services against national minimum standards[44,45,46] and will have powers of enforcement to make sure that services meet required standards.

Assessing performance

Performance indicators on a wide range of NHS activities and objectives – based on the national performance assessment framework (PAF) – have been published annually for the past three years. In 2001, the Department of Health published a league table of acute trusts in England, with rankings based on a composite of a selected number of performance indicators (*see* box *below*).[47] Each trust was given a 'star rating' between zero and three.

Performance rating criteria

Organisations are assessed across four main areas:

1. Key targets
- Inpatient waiting
- Outpatient waiting
- Long inpatient waits
- Breast cancer waits
- Financial performance
- 12-hour + trolley waits
- Cancelled operations
- Treatment of staff
- Hospital cleanliness

2. Clinical focus
- Clinical negligence
- Emergency readmission
- Deaths in hospital

3. Patient focus
- Inpatient waiting (time)
- Outpatient waiting (time)
- 4-hour + trolley waits
- Complaints resolved

4. Staff focus
- Sickness/absence
- Junior doctor's hours
- Consultant vacancies
- Nurse vacancies
- Allied health professional vacancies

High performance on the star rating system (attaining three stars) has subsequently been rewarded not with extra money (a system that would be open to the accusation that to those that have most will be given more) but by a greater degree of freedom so called 'earned autonomy'.[48] This initially meant that a three-star trust had more freedom over how to spend its share of a national (and evenly divided) performance fund, although it has now been extended to possible new freedoms from regular inspection or the constraints of being a state-owned organisation.[49]

As well as incentives for those that performed well on the star system, the Government also introduced disincentives for those who did badly. Zero stars were to put the organisation on a last chance status with chief executives given three months before they and their management team were sacked and replaced – either from a more successful organisation within the NHS or even from the private sector in a process which (rather misleadingly) has been called franchising. The first round of star ratings produced 12 trusts with zero star ratings. Four have now been taken over by alternative NHS management teams.[50]

The actions taken to reform the system of professional regulation have been a mix of Government threat and professionally driven response.

The wide-ranging Bristol Inquiry recommended that the monitoring of clinical performance at a national level should be brought together and co-ordinated by a new independent Office for Information on Healthcare Performance located within CHI. The NHS Reform and Health Care Professions Bill, currently before Parliament, proposes to establish such an office. Its duties will include both the collection and analysis of data and the assessment of performance against criteria to produce star ratings. The Department of Health is working with CHI to refine and improve the criteria for assessing performance in the future.

Improving organisational performance

Here, too, new national organisations have been given the remit of turning policy intent into practice. Established respectively in April and July 2001, the Modernisation Agency [51] and the National Patient Safety Agency [52] are in their early days.

The Modernisation Agency

The Modernisation Agency aims to provide targeted and expert support to the work of service improvement and local service development. In many ways the agency is an umbrella organisation bringing together previous initiatives to promote and support organisational learning, achievement, leadership and improvement. It encompasses the National Patient Access Team, the primary care development team, collaborative programmes for cancer, coronary heart disease, mental health, primary care, critical care, orthopaedics, recruitment and retention, and the Clinical Governance Support Team. All this sits alongside an effort to co-ordinate the provision of leadership development for more than 30,000 leaders and managers of the NHS. The Government is now targeting the efforts of the Modernisation Agency at those organisations who perform badly under the star rating system.

The National Patient Safety Agency

The National Patient Safety Agency is the Government's practical response to the promises to better manage adverse events. It is charged with introducing a mandatory national system for identifying, recording, analysing and reporting failures, mistakes and near-misses in the health service. It will collect and analyse information on adverse events and by the end of 2002, all NHS trusts and most primary care trusts are expected to provide information to the national system. Its objective is to draw conclusions from that information and feed them back into practice, service organisation and delivery.

Assuring clinical performance

The actions taken to reform the system of professional regulation have been a mix of Government threat and professionally driven response. The professional regulatory bodies have promised action to ensure greater accountability, transparency and efficiency. Their proposals include the greater involvement of lay people in their governance, simpler and quicker processes for the investigation of concerns about professional performance or conduct, and the development of methods for the periodic revalidation of every professional's fitness to practice.[53] However, the Government has forced the pace and made it clear that it is prepared to use its powers to intervene more directly if it is not content with the direction or speed of change.[54]

The Government's first action was to introduce new legislation, not directly to reform the professional regulators, but to make potential future Government reform of the statutory regulators of health care professionals easier to initiate and drive through Parliament.[55] The move was widely interpreted as laying the ground for more direct intervention if the professional regulators did not deliver an agenda for reform that matched Government objectives.

In 2000, the Government consulted on proposals and draft orders for just such a revamp of the structures for regulating nurses, midwives and health visitors, and for the organisation responsible for regulating thirteen other health care professional groupings.[56,57] These provided a clear model for the medical profession to follow. Broadly, the reforms followed the guidance later articulated in *The NHS Plan* that required the self-regulatory bodies to be smaller, with much greater patient and public representation, to have faster, more transparent procedures and to develop meaningful accountability to the public and the health service.

Council for the Regulation of Health Care Professionals

In addition, in 2001, the Government set out plans for an over-arching body to oversee the work of each of the professional regulatory bodies.[58] The Council for the Regulation of Health Care Professionals (CRHCP) is intended to co-ordinate the work of the different bodies, ensuring that they employ similar standards to judge their members' work and that their procedures are transparent to the public. It is proposed that the Council also has the powers to investigate maladministration and, in extreme circumstances, to refer individual cases to appeal where it believes the regulatory body may not have acted in the public interest. The establishment of the Council is part of the National Health Service Reform and Health Care Professions Bill currently before Parliament.

National Clinical Assessment Authority

In April 2001, the Government established the National Clinical Assessment Authority (NCAA). This new body will provide assessments of clinical performance when employers raise concerns about an individual's practice.[59] The NCAA is now testing its methodology. The intention is that on the basis of clinical data, discussion with the doctor and other staff, and a visit, the authority's team of medical and lay assessors will make a judgement about the doctor's performance and recommend a course of action. In the first instance, responsibility for dealing with problem doctors will rest with employers, who will be expected to act on the assessment authority's recommendations, although they are not bound by them. In serious cases, the NCAA is likely either to recommend that the employer refer the doctor to the GMC to see whether their licence to practise should be revoked, or to make a referral itself.[60]

The impact of policy

The impact of each theme in Labour's approach to health care quality is addressed separately. However, initiatives to develop quality assurance and improvement are not self-serving ends in themselves but multiple means to the same end. Indeed, it may be hard to ascribe cause and effect, let alone absolute impact.

The full range of institutions with a role in quality improvement in the NHS is illustrated in Figure 24.

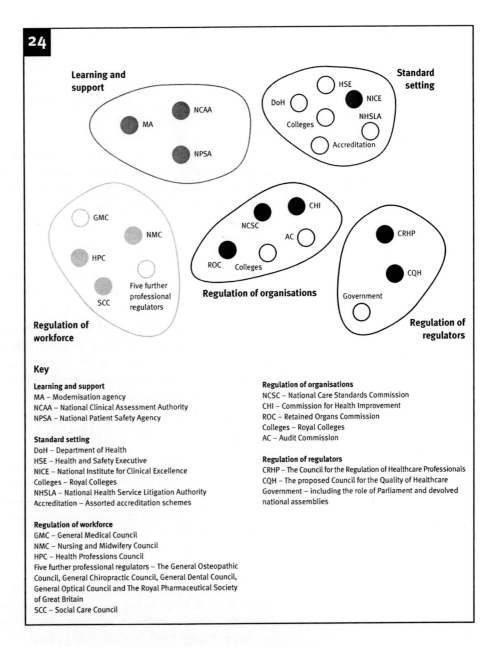

24

Learning and support
MA
NCAA
NPSA

Standard setting
HSE
DoH
NICE
Colleges
NHSLA
Accreditation

Regulation of workforce
GMC
NMC
HPC
SCC
Five further professional regulators

Regulation of organisations
NCSC
CHI
AC
ROC
Colleges

Regulation of regulators
CRHP
CQH
Government

Key

Learning and support
MA – Modernisation agency
NCAA – National Clinical Assessment Authority
NPSA – National Patient Safety Agency

Standard setting
DoH – Department of Health
HSE – Health and Safety Executive
NICE – National Institute for Clinical Excellence
Colleges – Royal Colleges
NHSLA – National Health Service Litigation Authority
Accreditation – Assorted accreditation schemes

Regulation of workforce
GMC – General Medical Council
NMC – Nursing and Midwifery Council
HPC – Health Professions Council
Five further professional regulators – The General Osteopathic Council, General Chiropractic Council, General Dental Council, General Optical Council and The Royal Pharmaceutical Society of Great Britain
SCC – Social Care Council

Regulation of organisations
NCSC – National Care Standards Commission
CHI – Commission for Health Improvement
ROC – Retained Organs Commission
Colleges – Royal Colleges
AC – Audit Commission

Regulation of regulators
CRHP – The Council for the Regulation of Healthcare Professionals
CQH – The proposed Council for the Quality of Healthcare
Government – including the role of Parliament and devolved national assemblies

Setting national standards – a mixed picture

CHI is obliged to conduct formal evaluations, working alongside the Audit Commission, in the implementation of National Service Frameworks, but, to date, the only completed study is on cancer care. This study looks at how well the NHS has met the recommendations of the 1995 Calman/Hine report on the delivery of local cancer services and is only a baseline against which the success of this Government's National Cancer Plan can be assessed. However, it provides an insight into the progress that the National Service Framework is making on delivering national objectives – and the picture is mixed. On the one hand, it reports significant progress on some national targets: for example, 92 per cent of patients referred urgently by GPs are now seen within two weeks – a significant step toward the 100 per cent target – although this needs to be seen in the wider perspective offered by Chapter 3 on waiting list targets in general. Survival rates for most cancers are improving and there are more specialist cancer surgeons. On the other hand, it points out that 'improvement has been patchy, services lack co-ordination and the care patients can expect varies according to where they live and the type of cancer they have'.[61]

The role brought with it massively increased paperwork, an over-reliance on locum cover, neglect of their own professional development, and strained relationships with colleagues, patients, spouses and children.

Building clinical governance – patchy progress

Evidence about the implementation of clinical governance fits a similarly mixed pattern. A three-year study of clinical governance in primary care showed that, by January 2002, the process was becoming embedded in the day-to-day working lives of the 24 practices that were participating in the study. Members of the primary care teams and the clinical governance leads were viewing clinical governance as 'part and parcel' of their job. Primary care clinical governance leads could identify benefits to their own surgeries (for example, regular clinical meetings, significant event auditing), as well as advantages for the primary care organisation (for example, sharing anonymised data, and networking across previously isolated primary care teams).[62]

However, these leads also identified some negative consequences for themselves and problems in achieving clinical governance objectives for the organisation. For example, the role brought with it massively increased paperwork, an over-reliance on locum cover, neglect of their own professional development, and strained relationships with colleagues, patients, spouses and children. For the organisation, this lack of perceived support led to a high risk of burn-out and resignation on behalf of clinical governance leads. Interviewees emphasised the challenge of trying to achieve implementation alongside substantial organisational change (the move to trust status in particular) and a paucity of ear-marked funding. Many reported that the clinical governance role still did not come with clear accountability, infrastructure, or adequate support funding.[63]

In hospital, mental health and community trusts, it is harder to find sound and timely research evidence through which to assess impact. However, it is clear from the first 80 or so CHI reports that progress on clinical governance is patchy. Earlier studies in London and the West Midlands reported significant progress on establishing systems and processes for clinical governance activity within trusts, but doubts over the degree to which the agenda had really reached the clinical frontline. Both studies found clinical governance to be well received and found progress in the supporting structures and processes necessary to undertake the work, as well as serious attention being given to the quality agenda by the board.[64,65] This mixed set of findings is unsurprising given the comprehensive ambition of the programme and the culture change needed to facilitate its wholesale implementation.

Assessing performance – can the PAF claim credit for improvements?

Commenting on the most recent set of performance indicators, published in February 2002, the Department of Health stated that:

> 'The data published here show real improvements across most indicators [when 'current year' 2000/01 is compared against previous year 1999/ 2000]... Taken together, the quantitative and qualitative data from these indicators and the NHS Modernisation Board Report show that the programme of investment and reform contained in *The NHS Plan* is bringing about measurable improvements to NHS performance.' [66]

However, improvements in performance as revealed by the performance indicators in the performance assessment framework need to be interpreted with care as:

- Performance could improve because of 'performance indicator creep'. For example, managers may focus on quality improvement, and direct their managerial energy principally towards the dimensions of their activity captured by performance indicators, diverting their attention away from other aspects of their business. Thus, performance shifts between measured and unmeasured activities.

- Improvements may not be a result of performance measurement in itself but of changes in factors beyond the influence of the NHS, such as changes in society as a whole.
- The main focus of the existing performance information has been the year, as this is the usual time unit for data collection – but many aspects of performance vary within the year, while others change so slowly that annual change is small and likely to be masked by data error or variability. In some areas, such as financial performance, the annual cycle will remain important. But in others, the periods selected for *reporting* changes in performance need to be chosen with care. For example, the Department of Health reports that the proportion of patients who missed their first outpatient appointment fell by 1.5 per cent between 1999/2000–2000/01). Since 1997, however, it has increased, by 0.5 per cent.

Evaluating the outcome of the star rating system is difficult as the first wave of 'franchising' for zero starred trusts has only just begun, and it is also too early to judge the impact of 'earned autonomy' for three- and two-starred trusts. However, it would be surprising if the replacement of some trust chief executives did not have some positive impact on the performance of their trusts. But, as with the PAF, the reason for improvement may well not lie with the performance system (here, star rating, earned autonomy and 'franchising') but with other factors, not least the extreme focus of management and political attention on a handful of under performing trusts.

Improving organisational performance – a way to go

Despite the relative newness of the Modernisation Agency, the various initiatives under its ambit preceded their new organisational home. Yet evidence of impact is still thin. Certainly the level of participation in the various policy initiatives under this heading is impressive. Five thousand NHS staff are involved in the Cancer Service Collaborative, working to improve the quality and co-ordination of cancer services, and more than a thousand are involved in the Clinical Governance Support Team.[67] The Modernisation Board, an independent group created by *The NHS Plan* to take an overview of the modernisation process, claim in their annual report that 90 per cent of cancer collaborative projects have enabled patients to choose their own appointment time.[68] Yet, without formal or external evaluation, it is hard to put such headlines in context. Although the number of staff involved in their work is an unsatisfactory proxy for impact, the director of the Modernisation Agency commented that: 'currently less than 15 per cent of staff are estimated to be actively involved', compared with a stated aim of increasing this to 100 per cent.[69] That leaves some way to go.

Assuring clinical performance – planning radical reform

Not surprisingly, the reforming agenda of the GMC has broadly followed the Government's vision. Radical reform is proposed in three areas:

- the governance of the GMC [70]
- the way it investigates potential cases where a doctor may prove unfit to practice [71]
- proposals for the revalidation of each and every doctor on the professional register.[72]

The Government has been active, even hyperactive, in its approach to quality improvement and assurance.

These approaches to reform have a sound basis in principles of good corporate governance and current statements of good regulatory practice in fields other than health care. Action on revalidation is the most radical. But a process for judging the revalidation of all doctors will not be in place until 2004.

Once implemented, changes in professional regulation could have significant impact the process for revalidating all doctors, for example, could, for the first time, bring effective scrutiny to bear on individual clinical performance, knowledge and behaviour. Alternatively, of course, the process could prove to be less meaningful based more on compliance with a paper exercise than on offering a robust challenge.

The new Council for the Regulation of Health Care Professionals (CRHCP) is still to be established, and the work of the National Clinical Assessment Authority is not yet in full flow. The Bristol Inquiry has already underscored the need for greater co-ordination between the multiple systems for professional regulation, redress and organisational learning.[73] Similarly, when addressing the regulation of health care organisations, the Inquiry called for greater co-ordination of organisations such as the National Care Standards Commission (which still has to start the work of inspection) and CHI (which is yet to initiate a proposed evaluation of the impact of its work).

If a modern system of regulation for health care professionals and organisations is to lead (rather than follow in the wake of) a new relationship between the public, professionals and the state, implementation needs to occur quickly. Given the current half-implemented nature of reform it is not possible to assess impact, although it is not too early to worry that the positive potential of proposed change might be tarnished by delay.

Conclusions

New organisations

The Government has been active, even hyperactive, in its approach to quality improvement and assurance. However, the focus of this energy has been on establishing quangos and giving them the responsibility for action. Putting these organisations in place takes time and money, and risks confusion as their new roles and responsibilities emerge. It is also an approach that delays real impact on those who work in the NHS and how they go about that work.

Developing a body of work

The more established organisations, such as NICE and CHI, have developed a body of work that is amenable to evaluation. They have been operational long enough to have developed a relationship with the NHS. Criticisms of NICE are developed in Chapter 4 but, in brief, the process used for the assessment of new treatments still lacks clear transparency in relation to the criteria for cost effectiveness.

Evaluation

CHI has also developed a body of work and has built a direct relationship with the organisations that it has inspected. It will soon be commenting indirectly on every organisation in the health service through the performance assessment system. However, like NICE, there is still no formal evaluation of the quality or usefulness of its work, or its impact on the organisation at the receiving end. The difficulty for CH and many other new or reformed organisations that seek to influence the NHS, such as the Modernisation Agency is that they have yet to develop effective ways of co-operating so that inspection and review are followed through with development and improvement. For those who fair badly on inspection, performance assessment or star rating, it is imperative that action and improvement follows quickly, otherwise the process risks demoralising staff, exacerbating existing recruitment and retention problems, and starting a negative cycle rather than prompting positive change.

Taken as a whole, the conceptual framework that promotes national standard setting, accountability for local delivery and monitoring implementation is now uncontentious. However, the scale of the standard setting and monitoring enterprise attracts criticism. The work of so many national bodies and the obligations that they place upon NHS organisations seems to have been added to existing and extensive performance monitoring, rather than being considered as an alternative framework within which the service might be given a greater degree of freedom to deliver.

Spreading good practice

Growth of initiatives and action teams within the Modernisation Agency is evidence that there is no fear of experimentation in the search to find out what works. However, there seems to have been little premium put on rigorous, timely, independent and research-based evaluation. Such evaluation might have helped to establish the real impact and opportunity cost of the overarching framework for quality improvement and assurance that Labour has erected.

The verdict

The Government has introduced far-reaching reforms of the way quality is assured in UK health care. From the regulation of individual professionals to the assessment of whole organisations' performance, Labour's reforms could revolutionise the way the public judges the NHS and its workforce. However, it is still unclear how much they will affect the quality of care received by individual patients.

8 The private sector

Key issues:

- Building hospitals through the Private Finance Initiative
- Using private hospitals for NHS operations
- Making more use of private nursing and intermediate care

The inheritance

Moving towards privatisation

The use of the private sector to provide services to the NHS is one of the thorniest issues facing the Labour Government.

When Labour came to office, care in some parts of the NHS was already being provided by private organisations – most notably in mental health services where both charitable and profit-making bodies were providing a wide range of services. Health authorities already free to send patients to private hospitals for surgery, although few actually did. In 1997, nursing home provision was almost entirely in the hands of private suppliers following the unplanned switch of financial responsibility for those needing continuing nursing care to the social security budget in the early 1980s. A large share of hospital support services was also contracted out, as a result of policies introduced in the early 1980s. Hospitals themselves had always been built by the private sector, and the design capacity that had been in place within the DHSS up until the 1980s had largely been disbanded. Even that mainstay of the NHS, the general practitioner, was a private contractor, not an employee.*

In 1997, the private finance initiative (PFI) was stalled, with no major hospital building contract yet signed. The introduction of private finance across the whole of the public sector had begun in the first half of the 1990s but took off slowly within the NHS, with the exception of minor schemes such as provision of car parking or incinerators. The Conservatives had hoped to be able to announce completed deals before the 1997 election but, while a number of major hospital schemes were almost at the point of closure, private sector concerns about the risks they were taking on prevented them from being finalised.

The policy pledges

The 1997 Labour Manifesto made it clear that while the party would do what was necessary to make the private finance initiative work effectively, it opposed the privatisation of clinical services – which the Conservatives were accused of promoting. Labour's first health White Paper,[1] published later that year, reaffirmed this position.

---

* As were dentists, pharmacists and opticians working in community settings.

It was entirely focused on the NHS: the private sector was not mentioned as a care provider.

Encouraging private provision through *The NHS Plan*

On assuming power, Labour did not try to 'claw back' privately provided services into the NHS: in effect, they were ignored or taken for granted. Nor was any positive incentive or instruction offered to encourage any further inroads by private providers into NHS services. Indeed, as late as 1999, the opposite was true. But from *The NHS Plan* onwards, a different policy emerged: for both elective and intermediate (including nursing home) care, the Government positively encouraged the use of private facilities and provided extra cash to buy operations from privately owned hospitals.

By 2002, the private sector was actively encouraged to extend its role in the provision of care as well as support services (for example, in early 2002 contracts for the supply of pathology services by the private sector were announced). In a speech given in January 2002, the Secretary of State, Alan Milburn, appeared to be opening up the provision of health care services to a wide range of public and private organisations, under the aegis of a 'values-based' NHS rather than a single 'nationalised industry'.[2]

When Labour took power, the need for a substantial hospital building programme was largely unchallenged. The NHS had suffered from cutbacks in capital spending since the mid-1970s when the International Monetary Fund visitation put paid to the implementation of the capital programme agreed in the previous decade.[*] Capital spending had fallen and, as a result, the condition of the stock worsened: an enormous backlog of repairs built up.[3]

But, while the need for extra spending appeared urgent, the case for using private finance was far from clear. In 1997, the Government was anxious to reduce its borrowing level to bring it into line with EU conditions for entry into the Euro. Using private finance enabled it to keep borrowing down while rapidly expanding the hospital building programme.

Over time, because of rapid improvement in public finances, that argument lost strength, leaving the case for the policy to be made in 'value-for-money terms': in short was procurement via the private sector more effective than the traditional method? In supporting the use of private finance in 1997, the then Secretary of State, Frank Dobson, poured scorn on the traditional method, citing massive overruns in terms of time and cost on (one or two) schemes.[4] Using private finance was expected to keep scheme costs under control and ensure that the new hospitals were built on schedule.

The Government's actions

Extending the Private Finance Initiative

To remove the logjam they inherited in the PFI, Labour passed the NHS 1997 Act, which allayed the fears of the private sector that contracts entered into with trusts might not be honoured. In June 1997, the then Health Minister, Alan Milburn, was

---

[*] The first major hospital building programme since the foundation of the NHS began with the 1962 Hospital Plan for England and Wales (revised 1966).

The Government has been able to claim, accurately, that the largest ever hospital building programme is underway.

able to announce that a number of schemes would go ahead and since then further waves have been approved. As a result, the Government has been able to claim, accurately, that the largest ever hospital building programme is underway.[5] Major new hospitals have already been built in Carlisle, Norwich, Dartford (in Kent) and Greenwich (in London), with many more to follow. By 2001, the overall value of schemes constructed or in planning had reached £7.5 billion (*see* Table 4).

Table 4: Capital value of major schemes given go-ahead since 1 May 1997	£ million capital value
PFI schemes completed and operational	297
PFI Schemes reached financial close with work started on site	1,578
Other Prioritised PFI schemes	5,488
Publicly funded schemes completed and operational	48
Publicly funded schemes with work started on site	124
Total major investment given the go-ahead	**7,535**

Source: Department of Health. *Departmental Report*. London: The Stationery Office, 2001

Only a fraction of these had been or were being procured and financed in the conventional way. New hospital building was therefore completely dominated by private finance. However, smaller schemes, including major equipment purchases, continued to be paid for out of public funds and, even by 2001/02, over half of total capital spending was financed in this way.

Improving primary care premises

In contrast to hospitals, community health facilities are generally small and relatively simple to build. But, in many parts of the country, particularly inner city areas, GPs and others have always operated from out-of-date and unsuitable premises. Nevertheless, it was not until 2000 that a new initiative known as LIFT (Local Investment Finance Trust) was announced in the *NHS Plan* to develop public–private partnerships to provide primary care premises. In July 2001 the LIFT prospectus was eventually published. It set out, in very brief terms, proposals for a new form of local investment agency. The *NHS Plan* indicated that the aim was to produce some £1 billion in new facilities, involving the refurbishment or replacement of surgeries for some 3,000 GPs and the creation of 500 'one-stop' primary care centres, with the initial focus on inner-city areas.

The LIFT prospectus identified the need for an increased level of investment in terms that would command broad agreement. The standard of existing premises is often low. In many areas very little new investment has taken place, and, where it does, it tends to be piecemeal. The prospectus also points out that GPs face significant disincentives to practise in inner-city areas – leases are too restrictive but if they invest in new premises they face the risk of negative equity.

However while the case for spending more might be clear, as with hospitals, the prospectus does not attempt to justify the particular means proposed for financing it. Nor has any other Government statement. The Government is nevertheless pressing ahead with the development of LIFT companies – so far two waves of LIFT areas have been identified, the majority in inner city locations – and it appears to have no thought for piloting the new approach nor providing for its evaluation. However, despite its haste, no local LIFTs are fully operational as yet.

Using private clinical and nursing care

The *NHS Plan*[6] referred to a 'national framework for partnership between the private and voluntary sector and the NHS' bearing on elective, critical and intermediate care. In November 2000, the Government published the Concordat,[7] which set out what the framework would involve. This brief document set out in very general terms a broad brush agreement between the Government and the private and voluntary sectors. It pointed to the need to involve the private sector in capacity planning, staffing requirements and local service development. But it did not deal with these issues in a substantive way. In the following year, the Labour Manifesto stated that the private sector might be brought in to manage the 'specially built surgical units' which had been announced in *The NHS Plan* but did not specify precisely how and when this might be done.

The Government has not published any data and, at the time of writing at the time of writing is in the process of checking the extent to which individual trusts have made use of private facilities. It is clear, however, that the contribution of the private sector (including hospitals in other EU countries*) is tiny – a few tens of thousands of operations set against a total of some 5.5 million.*

In contrast, intermediate or nursing home care* is almost entirely in the hands of the private sector. In October 2001, the Government published a new Agreement, entitled *Building Capacity and Partnership in Care*[8] which, in the words of the Secretary of State's foreword, 'makes the beginning of a new and more positive partnership between the statutory and independent social and health care and housing sectors'. The Agreement argues that commissioning bodies should invest more ambitiously in private providers to help to shape the market for care services in their localities.

The impact of policy

Building new hospitals

Against the yardstick of speedy and efficient delivery, the use of private finance has been a success: schemes have generally been delivered on time and within budget.* As a result, the NHS and its patients are already experiencing the benefits of a number of new hospitals with the firm prospect of many more to come.

However, this comparison, good enough for Parliamentary debate, distorted the average experience of public sector procurement: the cited schemes were far from typical.[9] In most cases, overruns after final scheme costs had been agreed were less than 10 per cent. Furthermore, evidence to a Commons Health Committee inquiry showed that procurement by the public sector could be well managed even in very difficult circumstances.[10]

In addition, there is no doubt that the cost of negotiating the first wave of schemes was very high. Both those procuring new hospitals and those seeking to supply

---

* Following a decision by the European Court the Government supported the use of hospitals in other EU countries for patients on the waiting list: the first few went to France in January 2002.

* The NHS does more operations than this, but some are emergencies which would not be done in private facilities.

* The term 'intermediate care' is hard to define precisely. Here we use it to refer to services offered outside people's homes although, in some contexts, it may also be used to refer to home-based care.

* However, in some cases, eg, Norfolk and Norwich, scheme costs have risen substantially since the first estimates.

The gains from using private finance are modest, typically amounting to a few per cent of total scheme costs.

them were entering into uncharted waters so the negotiations were understandably slow and expensive. The Department of Health subsequently took a number of steps to reduce these transactions costs, for example, by developing standard clauses for use in all private finance contracts. But even now, the private sector still finds the process onerous and expensive.[11] The nature of the bidding process is inherently costly to both public and private sectors.

However, the long-term implications are more important. The use of private finance entails higher borrowing costs since the Government can borrow at a lower rate than any private company. To offset these higher costs, private sector companies have had to produce savings in the costs of building and maintaining hospitals over the longer term. In principle, before a scheme is approved, the trust proposing it has to demonstrate that the price at which the private sector can build and make a hospital available is lower than what it would cost to do the job itself.

These calculations have been challenged on a number of grounds.[12] Of these the most serious is that trusts proposing schemes have systematically biased them to ensure that the private option came out superior to the public. Their motive for doing so is obvious enough: they believed that access to public finance was so limited that the chances of having their scheme funded that way were minimal.

This charge has been strenuously denied by the Government.* But what is clear is that even if the calculations are taken at their face value, the gains from using private finance are modest, typically amounting to a few per cent of total scheme costs.* For example, the difference between the private and publicly funded options for provision of the new Swindon and Marlborough Trust hospital was less than £1 million. While other schemes promise larger gains, this scheme is far from unique.

In fact, modest gains were only to be expected. Labour declined to allow the private sector to provide clinical services – which account for some 70 per cent of hospital costs – so the scope for achieving lower costs was limited. In many cases, services such as catering and laundry, which make up the remaining 30 per cent, had already been put out to tender as a result of the policies introduced by the Conservatives in the 1980s, and so were already subject to private sector competitive pressures.

Essentially, therefore, the case for using private finance rests not so much on the belief that specific levels of efficiency gains will accrue, but rather on the general belief that the incentive structure facing the private sector provider is more likely to achieve the stated level of costs than the public sector is of achieving the level it promised. In fact the incentive structure is the key innovation: by linking all the phases of hospital provision – design, building and operating – an incentive is created to provide buildings with an eye to their long-run maintenance costs. The traditional method can in principle be designed and built with a view to minimising lifetime costs but it cannot create the same long-term financial framework given by the private finance initiative.

By definition, however, this argument cannot be validated by the experience of the past five years nor, probably, can it ever be. Because the Government has made the PFI almost universal, the basis of comparison will not exist.

---

* Evidence from trusts given to the Health Select Committee would seem to confirm it was true however.
* Gains in other sectors, eg, prisons have been greater: in this case the private providers offer the whole service, ie, they provide staff as well as facilities which offers greater scope for savings.

What is clear is that the NHS has rushed into a massive capital building programme without any collective or central reflection as to precisely what type of facilities it ought to be investing in.

If the merits of the policy rest on the long-term issues, other considerations come into play. Labour's hospital building programme was launched into a strategic vaccuum.[13] It was only in September 1998 that the National Beds Inquiry was commissioned by a Secretary of State worried about the NHS's capacity to cope with winter peaks of demand, and the results of this work were not published until February 2000,[14] when several billion pounds had already been committed.

The National Bed Inquiry attempted to estimate whether or not more acute hospital beds were needed. But it did not deal with most of the factors relating to changes in the type and size of hospital services we need, including changes to junior doctors' hours, increasing medical specialisation and concerns about the safety of smaller hospitals. Since the Inquiry was published, the Department of Health has not published a document responding to these issues.

In other words, whether the hospitals being built are the hospitals we are likely to need in 10, 20 or 30 years time is unclear, given the scope for shifting many services to other locations and the trend towards the centralisation of key functions such as emergency care.[*] This issue is especially pertinent to the PFI because NHS trusts are tied into deals with the companies who build and maintain their facilities for 30 years, which may reduce the flexibility they have to respond to change in need, or increase the costs of any alterations. So while the need for new investment may be clear, how it should be deployed is much less obvious. These uncertainties[16] cast doubt on the wisdom of entering into long-term contracts. The contracts under which hospitals are provided do allow for some degree of flexibility, but it remains unclear what costs a trust would incur if it had to close or restructure a significant part of its facilities – and whether those costs will represent a barrier to change in future.

What is clear is that the NHS has rushed into a massive capital building programme without any collective or central reflection as to precisely what type of facilities it ought to be investing in.

Using 'spare capacity'

The *NHS Plan* promised more staff and other necessary resources, but none could be provided quickly. Accordingly, the attractions of using spare capacity in the private sector were clear.

But 'spare capacity' is a short- rather than long-term notion. It does not provide the basis for the kind of relationship the Plan appeared to envisage. The Plan did, however, propose the development of a number of new elective care and diagnostic centres, in association with the private sector, which do imply a long-term commitment. By the time of writing, no agreements had been reached, but active negotiations were underway with BUPA to transform Redwood Hospital, in Redhill, Surrey, into a diagnostic and treatment centre.[17]

The Government's approach to private nursing care remains similarly vague. The Agreement does not have anything to say about the underlying economics of the private sector organisations to which it is to apply, in particular whether the public sector commissioners will be able to provide the long-term security to give the private sector the confidence to continue to invest in the market. Nor does it tackle

---

* In public, at least, the Department of Health has shown no interest in these issues; by contrast, the Foresight programme under the aegis of the Office of Science and Technology has done so.[15]

the question of how competition between providers is to be handled. If the market is to be non-competitive then some of the advantages of private provision will be lost. If it is to be competitive, the process by which long-term contracts are awarded, and the implications for those who do not receive them, need more consideration. This issue lies buried within the vagueness of the term 'partnership'.

Conclusions

The role of the private sector

The private sector role in 2002 is not much different to what it was in 1997, and it will not be for some time that significant change occurs, even allowing for the measures announced by the Secretary of State. The one apparent exception is the provision of new hospital buildings, which is now almost entirely achieved through the use of private finance. But even here, change is less than it may seem. Hospitals have always been built by private sector companies and, since the 1980s, often maintained by them as well. However, the use of private finance does represent a new approach to the provision of health capital and in terms of getting hospitals built, it proved successful: whether it will prove so in the longer term is much less clear.

Change in the use of private providers for health and care services has been modest, in part because the shift in policy did not become apparent until well into Labour's first term. Therefore, in these areas, there is little practical experience to assess. To date, it appears that Labour has not succeeded in defining what the roles of public and private providers should be in these two areas.

A lack of trial and evaluation

At the level of rhetoric, there has been a distinct change in policy towards the private sector in the last five years. That change has not been justified by a general, ideological preference for private provision in terms the Conservatives might have used. Instead, the mantra has been 'what matters is what works'. Yet the Government has not tried to demonstrate that its policies are better than those they replaced.

In respect of the PFI and LIFT, the Government has entered, or plan to enter into, a series of long-term relationships, without a period of trial marriage in the form of evaluated pilots. Worryingly, the Government has responded to the heavy criticism it has received with impatience rather than reflection.[18]

Although it has taken a number of sensible measures to reduce the transaction costs associated with new hospital schemes and to encourage them to be developed within the content of the whole local health economy, it has not made a serious attempt to address the long term concerns that have been expressed about the current regime. One of the biggest such concerns is around whether the substantial risk involved in projects like building a new hospital is, in fact, being transferred to the private sector, and how this can be valued in economic terms.

A lack of clear definitions and data

In the provision of clinical and nursing services, the Government has expressed a wish to put the existing fitful relationship onto a better footing, but it has not been able to define what the nature of the long-term relationship might be. In the case of

So far, at least, no reasons have been put forward justifying the view that the private sector may be better placed than the public to provide the expertise which a 'failing' hospital requires.

nursing homes, where the private sector is well established, recent developments do suggest the need for better 'market management'. But the Agreement does not provide a sufficient basis for that: it contains no analysis either of the way that the market works now, how it may work in future, nor of what is needed for its effective management in terms of national and local expertise.

In the case of elective care, the Government has published no data on the costs of producing more operations within the NHS compared to the private sector. It has specifically declined to publish the costs of using hospitals in other parts of the EU.[19] At the current level of purchasing from the private sector at home and abroad, this does not matter greatly: given the pressing need to reduce waiting times and the difficulty of rapidly increasing NHS capacity in the short term, it is hard to argue against what the Government is currently proposing.

But the longer-term policy remains to be defined. If the private sector were to become a major provider, issues that have been put to one side would come to the fore:

- How exactly should the staffing issues be dealt with?
- Would it possible to ensure that increases in private sector capacity were not at the expense of reductions in the NHS?
- Should private hospitals pay for their nurses' training and, if so, on what basis?[20]
- Does it matter what range of work is carried out in the private sector, and, in particular, what would the impact be on the quality of care offered by NHS hospitals if the private sector were to employ full time consultants (or equivalent) out of an effectively fixed labour supply?

In other words, while the Government has claimed that the purpose of the Concordat and the Agreement is to provide the basis of a long-term relationship, in fact neither have yet succeeded in doing so. Nevertheless, they do hint at fundamental change.

Moving towards a range of different providers

In a speech[21] given in January 2002, the Secretary of State referred to changing the NHS from 'a monolithic, centrally run, monopoly provider to a values-based system where different health care providers – in the public, private and voluntary sectors – provide comprehensive service to NHS patients within a common ethos'. He added that where a particular hospital was performing badly the so-called franchise for its management might go to some non-NHS body such as 'a university, or a charity or to some other external management team' – with the latter clearly opening the door to the private sector.

This speech, which aroused an unfavourable response within the ranks of Labour supporters, has yet to be reflected in specific policy proposals. So far, at least, no reasons have been put forward justifying the view that the private sector may be better placed than the public to provide the expertise which a 'failing' hospital requires.[22]

But the speech appears[23] to open the way for a radically different NHS, which maintains the current objectives of providing care free at the point of access on the basis of need and not ability to pay, but where provision lies with a range of different bodies.

There is a case for going down this road – one which the authors of the Conservatives' 1989 White Paper [24] would recognise. It may, for example, improve patient choice, create some degree of competitiveness, or allow lessons about good practice to be learned between different sectors. But the Government has not provided either a vision of the future to which this road might lead nor a route map for journeying along it. In sum, policy towards the private sector lacks substantive practical or principled justification. On February 6th 2002, *The Times* [25] reported that the Government was preparing to publish a 'new vision' for the NHS, for publication in the run-up to the next election: all the greater is the need for that justification.

The verdict

The Government's enthusiasm for involving the private sector in the NHS is insufficiently grounded in evidence. It has gambled that what is built today with private finance will be fit for purpose in a decade or more. Its plans for greater private sector involvement in provision remain unclear. Is it looking to the private sector for expertise it believes the public sector lacks, or hoping private companies will provide a greater stimulus to service improvement? While the case for using spare capacity in the short term is obvious, the Government has failed to define what kind of longer-term relationships it wants to build with the private sector.

9 Long-term care

Key issues:

- Changing the way long-term care is funded
- Making better connections between health and social services
- Improving the quality of long-term care services

The inheritance

A legacy of problems

When the Labour Government came into office in 1997, it faced three main problems afflicting services providing care and support for people with long-term illnesses or disabilities:

- A funding system combining free health care and means-tested social care, which was widely perceived to be unfair, especially to older people who were having to sell their homes in order to pay for their care.
- The system of services provided by local government, the NHS, private and voluntary bodies was not working well for users and carers, who tended to get caught up in disputes between health and social care authorities as to who was responsible (or not) for their care. Unilateral action on the part of either the NHS or local authorities could also create blockages and other pressures in other parts of the system.
- Protection of vulnerable people using care services was regarded as inadequate, leaving users exposed to incompetence, neglect and abuse.

Labour has not been the only government having to face such problems. These have been long-running themes throughout the history of community care, with some difficulties originating in the post-World War Two settlement regarding the welfare state. However, there is no doubt that problems relating to funding, integration and quality had been exacerbated by successive Conservative governments during the 1990s – usually by default rather than by design.

An unfair funding system

The funding system for long-term care was established in the 1940s, when the NHS was set up and the rules enabling local authorities to assist frail older people and others were agreed. However, by the mid-1990s, the system had become very unpopular and there were calls for reform.

In the early 1990s, the Conservative Government had closed a loophole that allowed thousands of people opting to live in care homes to receive Income Support to offset the costs of their care. Under the NHS and Community Care Act 1990, access to public funding depended on an assessment made by local authorities, which would decide both about the need for a care home placement and an individual's ability to pay towards the cost of their care. More people than ever before found themselves being means tested. This included homeowners, some of whom had been encouraged to purchase their houses by a Conservative Government keen on creating a home-owning democracy. They found themselves having the value of their homes taken into account and the prospect of passing their assets to their children removed.

At the same time, many local authorities were charging for home care and other non- residential care services (as they were entitled to by law). They were compelled to do this as grants from central government were now calculated on the assumption that a proportion of local authorities' income would be raised through service charges. A complex system of charges emerged, with wide variations in charging policies and levels of fees.

The system was regarded as both complex and unfair. There was much talk of betrayal among older people and their carers, who felt they had paid taxes and National Insurance all their working lives and who expected the Welfare State to provide for them 'from the cradle to the grave'. This public outcry prompted John Major's Government to look seriously at insurance and equity release schemes that might protect people against the risk of needing long-term care.[1]

A fragmented system of care

Services for people with long-term illness and disability had long been provided by many different organisations, including the NHS, local authorities, voluntary organisations and private businesses. By 1997, the whole service system had become very fragmented, with serious turf wars breaking out between the NHS and local authorities about their responsibilities, and users and carers described as being caught in the crossfire.

The Conservative Government had attempted to clarify the respective responsibilities of the NHS and local authorities for the care of elderly and disabled people in the NHS and Community Care Act.[2] Local authorities were given lead responsibility for financing and arranging care, and the NHS was required to participate in the planning of local services. However, there was a grey area regarding people with 'continuing health care needs' who found themselves at the centre of disputes about who was responsible for their care.

With many hospitals having reduced their continuing care beds, the NHS was perceived as withdrawing from long-term care and shunting both patients and costs over to local authorities. Collaboration between the NHS and local authorities was weak and marred by cross boundary disputes. The Conservatives had to issue annual guidance on continuing care, spelling out what the NHS should provide and requiring both parties to agree on how they would deal with disputed cases.[3]

However, collaboration across boundaries was not made easier by a culture of competition that prevailed on both sides of the health and social care divide. On the one side, the NHS was operating an internal market, characterised by a separation of purchasers (health authorities) and providers (trusts). On the other side, local authorities were attempting to manage a mixed welfare economy, encouraging much greater use of independent providers. Unsurprisingly perhaps, it became more and more difficult to see how the whole system fitted together.

The system began to look dysfunctional, especially in winter periods, when hospital beds became 'blocked' by older people who no longer needed acute care but could not be discharged because of a shortage of intermediate, residential and home care.

The system began to look decidedly dysfunctional, especially during winter periods, when hospital beds became 'blocked' by older people who no longer needed acute care but could not be discharged because of a shortage of intermediate, residential and home care. Between 1992 and 2000, for example, Department of Health statistics show that the number of households receiving home care fell by 25 per cent, although the total number of contact hours increased as only people with the very greatest needs were offered help. In response to this problem, the Conservative Government began to provide special 'winter pressures' funding to help alleviate the blockages.[4]

An unsafe system

With regard to quality, there were no national standards of care. Regulation applied solely to residential and nursing home care, where standards focused largely on the physical fabric of the homes rather than the care provided. Inspections were carried out by both health and local authorities. There was much criticism of local authorities especially, who were not seen as independent and who were suspected of having double standards, requiring better quality care in independent care homes than that provided in their own care homes. Home care and other non-residential services were completely unregulated, even though home care providers themselves had been pushing for regulation in order to put a stop to 'cowboys' in the care business.[5]

Labour's predecessors declined to strengthen the regulatory framework. The Conservatives had placed great store on the merits of greater competition in the care sector, which would break the power of monopoly providers and lead to a more efficient and effective use of public money. The Government also tended to view regulation as bureaucratic red tape that would deter and hamper businesses operating within the mixed welfare economy.

The policy pledges

Setting up sustainable support

In its 1997 Manifesto, the Labour Party made several promises regarding long-term care. Its priority was to create 'real security for families through a modern system of community care'.[6] It pledged to set up a Royal Commission to work out a fair and sustainable system of funding long-term care. It also promised an independent inspection system and a long-term care charter to define the standards of services to which people could be entitled. Labour acknowledged that the system as a whole was not working well for people needing care and support, referring to community care as being 'in tatters'. However, no promises were made about creating a more integrated system of services.

Committing to health and social care partnerships

This position changed very quickly after Labour came into office. In the summer and autumn of 1997, the then Secretary of State, Frank Dobson, made a series of speeches outlining his determination to 'knock down the Berlin Wall that separates health and social services'. Time and again, he highlighted joint working as a priority for managing demand during the winter months.[7,8] A strategy quickly emerged, involving:

- directives instructing the regional offices of the NHS Executive and the Social Services Inspectorate to work together, spotting potential blockages in the system in advance and tackling them locally

- extra money for the NHS to spend on community services, aimed at reducing the numbers of delayed discharges from hospital and emergency admissions.

He also announced the Government's intention to legislate 'to make it easier for the NHS and social services to work together' by pooling their resources. These early statements demonstrated the new Government's commitment to health and social care partnerships, and heralded plans for bolstering collaboration through legal and financial incentives.

Promoting better health and greater independence

Before its second term in office, the Labour Party's promises about long-term care had shifted from the financial concerns that had been evident four years earlier, to a new focus on promoting better health and greater independence.[9] More money was promised for intermediate care and related services to ensure that older people would have *alternatives* to long-term care services. Where long-term care was mentioned, the emphasis was on improving access to a wide range of community services. There was also a promise to extend more control and choice to older people and carers over the services used, through Direct Payments that could be used to buy the care and support they wanted. (This measure was already available for younger disabled people). And, finally, there was a promise of greater support for carers, through increased financial benefits and more social care services, such as respite care. These pledges repeated commitments made in *The NHS Plan*, drawn up by the Secretary of State for Health in July 2000.[10]

The Government's actions

Creating a fair funding system

The Government delivered on its promise to set up a Royal Commission. Under the chairmanship of Stewart Sutherland, the Commission worked throughout 1998, completed its work within a year and published its report in March 1999.[11] Its recommendations are summarised in the box below.

Key recommendations of the Royal Commission on Long-Term Care

- Making all personal and nursing care free and funded through taxation.
- Continuing to means test contributions towards living and housing costs.
- Disregarding the value of people's homes for up to three months after admission to a care home.
- Raising the capital limits used to determine whether and how much individuals should pay towards their care.
- Extending Direct Payments to people aged 65 and over.

Two members of the Commission, Joel Joffe and David Lipsey, issued a Note of Dissent, in which they argued that it would be better to spend the money required to fund free personal care on improving services such as home care, prevention and rehabilitation. They argued that providing free personal care would only transfer resources to the better off who were already paying for their care, and eventually to their children through inheritance.

The Government took some time to respond. Nine months after the Commission's report was published, the new Secretary of State, Alan Milburn, announced that

The Commission's central recommendation about personal care was rejected, with a commitment made instead to invest more money in improving services for older people.

further consultations would be undertaken about the means test for residential care, the definition of nursing care, the development of long-term care insurance products and other issues relating to charges and benefits.[12]

The Government finally made its response to the Royal Commission in July 2000 (at same time as it published its *NHS Plan*).[13] This was more than a year after the Royal Commission had reported – a matter that caused some comment at the time by those who noted ruefully that it had taken the Government longer to decide what to do than it had for the Commission to carry out the investigation.

Many of the recommendations made by the Royal Commission were accepted by the Government, including making nursing care free in nursing homes, extending Direct Payments to older people, and changing some of the rules governing the means test. But the Commission's central recommendation about personal care was rejected, with a commitment made instead to invest more money in improving services for older people.

In November 2000, the Government went on to issue guidance on fair charges for home care.[14] Local authorities were directed to stop levying charges at a rate that reduced people's incomes below basic levels of Income Support. When assessing people's ability to pay, account should be taken of disability-related expenditure before assuming that disability benefits could be used to pay service charges.

Action was also taken on the vexed question of people having to sell their homes to fund residential or nursing home care. A system of deferred payments was introduced at the end of 2001, which enabled people to delay selling their homes.

Breaking down the 'Berlin Walls'

During its first five years in office, the Government introduced measures compelling authorities to work together, providing funds with attached conditions about joint work between health and social services, and building performance measures for both sectors into the Government's planning priorities and targets. The intention has been to move collaboration between the NHS and local authorities from the margins of statutory sector activity and into mainstream programmes and budgets.

The Government imposed a statutory duty of partnership between the NHS and local authorities as they fulfil their responsibilities for promoting the health and wellbeing of local communities. The Health Act 1999 also enabled authorities to pool budgets, to agree which of them should act as lead commissioners for particular services or care groups, and to establish joint teams under a single management. This removed the legal and financial barriers that many authorities claimed were inhibiting effective joint work.[15]

Disappointed that few authorities used the new powers, the Government decided on tougher measures, making the new 'flexibilities' mandatory in the Health and Social Care Act 2001.[16] The same legislation also allowed health and social services authorities to form new integrated organisations called Care Trusts. These could be formed voluntarily by authorities wishing to do so but the Government also had powers to impose Care Trusts on organisations seen to be failing to collaborate.

The Government also introduced joint planning priorities and targets during its early years in office, making it clear that it would judge the performance of both health and social services by their achievements in improving mental health services and increasing the provision of rehabilitation services for older people. Both the NHS and social services departments became subject to star ratings, indicating the extent to which they were succeeding or failing to meet government targets.

The big test for health and social care partnerships always comes in the winter months, when demand for services increases. The Government soon instigated an annual process of winter pressures planning, involving health and social services at national level (through the Department of Health's Winter Emergency Services Team) and at regional and local level (through joint service initiatives designed to avoid long trolley waits in hospital A&E departments and to reduce delayed discharges from hospital). Large sums of money were injected into the system each winter to facilitate this process.

Improving the quality of care

The Government has set up a new range of institutions charged with inspecting and regulating care services. It has adopted a series of national standards regarding care services and applying to particular groups of people. And, finally, it has put in place a number of task forces and implementation groups charged with putting the standards into practice.

The Government's Long-term Care Charter, produced in December 1999, was one of Labour's earlier attempts to improve the quality of care by arming users and carers with information about the standards they could expect from health, housing and social services. The Charter was a national framework for the development of local charters. It was left to local authorities, working with their partners in housing and health, to set out what would be provided and when, and to specify the standards that would be met in, for instance, the length of time aids and equipment would be delivered following an assessment.

Later measures included the establishment of the National Care Standards Commission (NCSC) to regulate care homes, private and voluntary hospitals or clinics and home care services. The Government set up the Social Care Institute of Excellence to assist in the task of putting into practice evidence of service approaches known to result in good outcomes for users and carers. The General Social Care Council came into being, charged with registering the social care workforce, and raising professional and training standards.

These new bodies sat alongside health counterparts like the Commission for Health Improvement, the National Institute for Clinical Excellence and the longer established medical and nursing professional bodies. Few links were made between the respective organisations and the result was a somewhat overcrowded field that threatened to present a real burden to the local agencies expected to improve the quality of care. Thus, before the new social care institutions came into operation, there was talk of merging some of the bodies 'in due course'.

National standards were set for residential and home care services that care agencies would need to meet in order to be registered by the NCSC and allowed to carry on providing services.[17,18] And a series of National Service Frameworks were developed, setting standards to be achieved by the NHS and local authorities in mental health services and in services for older people.[19,20]

Early signs indicate that the number of nursing home residents who will benefit financially may be far lower than the Government anticipated.

The impact of policy

A fair funding system?

There was widespread disappointment at the Government's final response to the Royal Commission from lay and professional groups who had supported the Commission's recommendations.[21,22,23,24] Hopes that the Commission would propose a fair and affordable system founded on a consensus were dashed. There was no consensus. Nor was there any radical transformation of the funding system that had given rise to so much dissatisfaction before Labour took office in 1997.[25]

A start was made in implementing the new policy on free nursing care in nursing homes from October 2001. Self-funding nursing home residents were assessed for the amount of care provided by a registered nurse that they needed. Three bands of payment were established, indicating high (£110 per week), medium (£70 per week) and low (£35 per week) levels of need. Having assessed people's needs, health authorities were expected to pay the nursing homes accordingly, with the residents then paying less for their care. But already there are signs of implementation problems, with reports of older people gaining little as nursing homes hold onto the money and increase fees.

The Government has claimed that these measures add up to a fairer system of funding long-term care, and that a 'major injustice in the system' has been corrected.[26] It has also claimed that the measures would benefit thousands of people, including about 35,000 people who would save up to £5,000 per year on the costs of staying in a nursing home, and around 30,000 people who would no longer be forced to sell their houses prematurely. It is too early to tell whether these figures prove to be realistic. However, early signs indicate that the number of nursing home residents who will benefit financially may be far lower than the Government anticipated.

A better-integrated health and care system?

The short-term funding increases provided to tackle winter pressures enabled some re-shaping of the whole service system to take place. The money was used by both health and social services to begin building a new set of services offering recuperation and rehabilitation to older people who might otherwise have had no choice but to use hospitals or care homes. A start had been made in breaking the 'vicious circle' that the Audit Commission had expressed concern about early on in the Government's term of office.[27]

Hundreds of new intermediate care schemes emerged, including short stay units in care homes and community hospitals; rapid response teams caring for people in their homes who might otherwise have had to be admitted to hospital; and community rehabilitation or re-enablement teams. However, the future of these new services was somewhat precarious, depending, as they did, on short-term winter pressures funding. A more secure future was promised after the National Bed Inquiry recommended an expansion of what it called 'intermediate care'[28] and the Government decided in July 2000 to commit £900 million over four years for the development of intermediate care.[29]

Despite these measures, blockages in the system worsened during 2001. The numbers of delayed discharges from hospital began to rise again, and health and social services talked about 'winter pressures' being a year round problem. The 'bed blocking' problem was partly caused by a shortage of care home places in some parts of the

By the end of 2001, there were warnings of a looming crisis in the care sector, which could only be averted by substantially increased investment in social care – in line with the rate of increase already agreed for the NHS.

country, as some care owners left the market or decided not to take publicly funded clients any more. Care home owners in the private and voluntary sectors were struggling as prices were being held down while new quality standards had to be met and staff shortages addressed; realising valuable land assets was a more attractive option to many of them. In addition, local authorities complained that they had insufficient funds to provide fully for all the people who no longer needed to be in hospital. Instabilities in the care market were threatening to de-stabilise the entire service system. Furthermore, the old culture associated with the 'Berlin Wall' days was beginning to re-emerge, with health and social services blaming each other for blocked beds.

Labour moved quickly to try to stabilise the situation. First, an Agreement about the relationships between public and private care sectors was published. [30] This Agreement, drawn up in 2001, encouraged the use of longer-term contracts for private and voluntary sector care providers, allowing them greater certainty and security. It also encouraged greater capacity planning at local level, with representatives of both public and private sectors working together on commissioning strategies. Second, another infusion of cash was provided to deal with the 'bed blocking'. This time, the money – £300 million over two years – was given to social services, in recognition of their financial difficulties.

The Government claims that great progress has been made in developing and improving partnerships between the NHS and local government. [31] But the Secretary of State for Health clearly continues to be frustrated by the problem of delayed discharges and by the 'confusion and uncertainty about where the responsibilities of health and social care begin and end'. [32]

More protection for users?

Within five years, the Government succeeded in putting in place a complex regulatory framework – most of which was expected to come into operation in April 2002.

Early efforts to improve the way health and social care agencies delivered their services ran into difficulties. The Long-term Care Charter left authorities to specify standards, but, in practice, many preferred to describe the services they were providing rather than set specific service standards that users could rely upon. [33]

Although later measures, such as national regulation of the care sector, show more potential for safeguarding standards and improving the quality of care provided, they also inevitably drove up the costs of care, leading to difficulties for commissioners and providers of care alike. Some care home owners, and others who anticipated difficulties in meeting the standards for upgrading buildings and training staff, left the business. Local authorities claimed they had insufficient funds to pay for improved quality services. By the end of 2001, there were warnings of a looming crisis in the care sector, which could only be averted by substantially increased investment in social care – in line with the rate of increase already agreed for the NHS. [34]

Conclusions

New laws, institutions and funding commitments

Labour's record over the last five years has been a story of ambitious plans to tackle long running problems, responding to mounting public concern and recognising that success in long-term care was inextricably bound up with its plans for 'saving the NHS'. In many important respects, Labour has changed the face of long-term care, with new laws, rules and regulations, with new institutions and with commitments of new monies for service developments.

Many of the changes will not come into effect until this year and beyond, so they have hardly had time to make a difference on the ground. There are, nevertheless, signs of success and failure that suggest what the future might look like.

An unfair, unsustainable funding system

The funding of long-term care will continue to be a problem, unless there is a change in policy. Already, there are signs of trouble for free nursing care, with reports of older people gaining little as nursing homes hold on to the money paid by health authorities and merely increase their fees in order to comply with the new standards set by Government. There are worrying reports of the poorest left with a pittance as 'pocket money'. Scotland and Wales are adopting different policies that stand as a reminder to the English that their system is less generous than those over the borders. Pressure groups continue to lobby for change and think tanks re-visit the policy to find ways of linking pensions and long-term care.[35] This is clearly a problem that is not going to go away. On this issue, the Government failed to achieve a better system that was markedly fairer (and agreed to be so) than the one it inherited.

Partnership working between health and social care

The whole system of care services is better integrated than it was in 1997, with far fewer outbreaks of 'turf wars' and much more evidence of health and social care staff routinely working together to plan, develop and provide services. This reflects Labour's strategy, which has gone well beyond simply exhorting authorities to work together and relying on joint planning mechanisms to achieve a more coherent service system. However, serious problems remain as gaps and pressure points in the system result in users and carers not receiving timely and appropriate support.

The promise of more intermediate care has still to be realised, with committed funds still to be invested over the next three years. Furthermore, the pressures on health and social care partnerships are intense. They are grappling with continuing re-organisation (of primary care and health authorities) that undermines joint working; attempting to manage instabilities in the care market; and striving to deal with demands on the hospital sector that attract the attention of politicians and the mass media.[36]

The need for greater investment and regulation

Efforts to safeguard and improve the quality of care look much more promising, provided that steps are taken to create a more coherent regulatory system across health and social care. Even so, there is a great risk that the whole venture will be seriously undermined by a failure to invest more in social care, ensuring that care providers are paid the necessary price to recruit, retain and train staff, and to provide the quality of care demanded by the new standards.

The verdict

The Government has not succeeded in establishing a fair and sustainable system for funding long-term care. It has removed some anomalies from the system, but may well create new problems in their place. Integration between health and social services is improving, and both are now better regulated than before to protect users from poor quality care. Progress could still be seriously impeded by acute shortages of funds for social care.

10 Patient and public involvement

Key issues:

- Giving the public more information about health care
- Making services more responsive to patients
- Extending patients' choices about their own treatment
- Involving citizens more actively in NHS decision-making processes

The inheritance

The Patient's Charter – publicising health information

Under the Conservatives, the public was, for the first time, given information about how well local health services were doing. District level performance indicators that had been introduced in 1983 as a management tool [1] were taken a step further in 1991 with the introduction of the Patient's Charter. This was the first vehicle for making information about health services available to the public. It also gave patients rights: new service standards were set in key areas such as maximum waiting times for operations. Hospitals were expected to report their performance against these standards. The Charter aimed to make services more responsive to patients' needs through the oxygen of publicity, shaming trusts into improving services where they performed below standard. Although the Charter was an important initiative, turning performance information from a management tool into public information, it was criticised, especially by NHS staff, for emphasising the public's rights without also stressing their responsibilities.

The Charter also set out what patients could expect if they were not satisfied with the NHS. In response to the 1994 Wilson report [2] the Conservatives had implemented a uniform procedure for responding to complaints. This set down national criteria for tackling complaints and put in place a two-stage system: complaints would initially be dealt with locally and, where complainants were not satisfied with the response they received, they could ask their health authority to set up an independent review panel. By the time Labour came to power, cracks were beginning to appear in the system. Local systems were of variable quality and many health authority areas were failing to hit their targets for dealing with complaints.

Demonstrating the impact of local people's views

Under John Major, there was a recognition that devolution of resources away from Whitehall to local purchasers could make local health services less democratically accountable. *Local Voices* [3] required health authorities, the 'champions of the people', to demonstrate that local people's views had had a tangible impact on purchasing decisions. Although the initiative had patchy influence and did not always match the broad aspirations of *Local Voices*, [4] some health authorities began to experiment with ways to involve local people in decision-making and priority-setting, for example, Citizen's Juries, focus groups and local health panels.

The new Government pledged to open up public services to greater public scrutiny.

Community health councils

Finally, Labour inherited community health councils (CHCs), set up in 1974 to oversee local health services, and to compensate for the reduction in local accountability created by the unification of health services outside local government. The Conservatives had contemplated getting rid of CHCs but this proved a reform too far and CHCs survived where many public interest quangos fell by the wayside. By the end of the Conservatives' term of office, plans were in the pipeline to reform, though not abolish, CHCs.

The policy pledges

Opening up public services to scrutiny

Labour's 1997 manifesto promised to 'save and modernise the NHS'.[5] The public would be able to judge the quality of health services through new targets against which hospitals' performance would be monitored. A reformed Patient's Charter would help to make services more responsive to the public's needs by shifting from basic output measures to standards – focusing on the quality and success of treatment.

The new Government pledged to open up public services to greater public scrutiny. Trust boards – of which a third were chaired by Conservative councillors, former Tory MPs or people who had strong links with the Conservative Party [6] – were to become more representative of local communities, and board meetings were to be held in public.

Planning a radical restructure of the NHS

Within the Government's first term of office, two major White Papers – *The New NHS* and *The NHS Plan* – were produced, outlining plans for a radical restructuring of the NHS.[7] These promised greater public involvement in setting local health service priorities, a new set of principles for decision-making about planning major changes; new structures to give patients and the public more influence over local services; and more support when things went wrong, including an overhaul of the complaints system. They also promised greater transparency in the NHS, giving the public more information about their health and about the performance of local NHS organisations. Information would no longer be an end in itself but would be used to help patients choose, in limited circumstances, which services they would use.

Promising greater patient choice

The 2001 Labour manifesto[8] promised more responsive services and greater patient choice about treatment. Patients would be able to choose the time of their hospital appointment, which would be booked directly by their GP. Any hospital that cancelled an operation on the day of surgery for non-clinical reasons would have to offer a new date within 28 days or fund the patient's treatment at the time – and hospital – of their choice. Subsequent announcements stated that this could, in certain parts of the country, include receiving treatment abroad.[9]

The Government's actions

Increasing public access to information

The Government extended and refined the initiatives that the Conservatives had put in place to make services more responsive and more transparent to the public.

The National Performance Assessment Framework (NPAF), announced in *The New NHS*, was introduced, giving clear national standards for key services at trust and health authority level. Standards have been revised so that they are more closely in line with patient preoccupations, including new standards on patient and carers' experiences. Three sets of NPAF indicators have been published nationally [10] receiving extensive media coverage. They have formed the largest part of the new 'star ratings' given to each hospital trust as an indicator of its overall performance. Finally, the independent inspectorate, the Commission for Health Improvement, was set up to assess the performance of individual trusts, and makes its findings available to the general public.

In addition to the standards in the NPAF, new systems have been set up to measure patients' experiences. The annual National Patients' Survey, announced in *The New NHS* has been in place since 1998 and has considered patients' views of general practice (1998) and coronary heart disease care (1999). Locally, biennial patients' surveys, announced in *The NHS Plan*, will be carried out in hospital trusts from 2002 before being applied to primary care trusts, enabling them to use patients' views to improve local services. From 2002, all trusts will have to publish patient prospectuses that will include data on trust services, performance against government targets and patient satisfaction. Trusts are also required to set out in their prospectuses what they have done to respond to issues raised by patients in local patients' surveys.

If the new performance assessment framework lays down what patients can expect from services, the revised Patient's Charter, issued in 2001, sets out patients' own responsibilities to the NHS. Following a review of the Patient's Charter, led by the then chairman and chief executive of Pearson Television, Greg Dyke, a new document, *Your Guide to the NHS*,[11] was published. In it, national performance targets for the NHS were, for the first time, set against the public's responsibility to protect their own health by eating well, not smoking and complying with any treatment they were given. Significantly, the document contained no reference to patients' rights.

Extending patient choice

A series of measures have been implemented to make the NHS more responsive to patients and to introduce greater choice. Although the abolition of fundholding limited the capacity of individual GP practices to expand the range of treatments they could offer, primary care groups and trusts began to widen access to treatment outside hospital, including diagnostic services and some minor surgery. Patients in these areas now have a choice over whether they are treated in primary care facilities or in a hospital for certain conditions.

The introduction of walk-in-centres and the NHS Direct health advice line announced in *The New NHS* as an alternative to traditional GP surgeries has also begun to increase choice for patients needing to use primary care services. Direct-booking schemes for hospital appointments, announced in *The NHS Plan*, are being extended across the country, although these will not be fully implemented until 2005.

More fundamentally, measures have been introduced to help meet national waiting time targets, including pilot schemes to use spare capacity in NHS, private and foreign hospitals to treat patients who have been waiting beyond national target times. Primary care groups on the south coast have already offered patients the choice of treatment in France, and a new fund is being made available from July 2002 to pay for patients who have waited for heart operations for more than six

Involving communities in making difficult decisions about service reconfigurations – most contentiously, the closure or downgrading of hospitals – is an important area where little progress has been made since 1997.

months to be treated elsewhere.[12] New patient care advisers will be made available to help patients to choose between different options.

Increasing public involvement

One of the Government's earliest actions in 1997 was to implement its pledge to ensure that trust chairs and non-executive directors must live locally and use NHS services, and to make trusts hold board meetings in public. This policy provoked controversy from the outset over accusations that Labour Party members were being appointed to a disproportionate number of newly vacated seats on NHS boards.

Steps have also been taken to involve patients and the public in decision-making across the NHS. *The New NHS* introduced a new requirement on health authorities to involve the public in developing Health Improvement Programmes (or HIMPs), and to ensure that new primary care groups and trusts had suitable mechanisms to involve the public in shaping their services, for example, by including a lay member on the board of each PCG.

The NHS Plan, and subsequent policy documents on public involvement in the health service, were still more ambitious in scope (*see* box *below*). Although some of the measures announced in guidance leading on from the NHS Plan are not yet in place, local authorities now have powers to scrutinise health services, including the power to call chief executives and other senior staff before their new scrutiny committees. New patients' forums in all trusts, including PCTs, will have rights of inspection over NHS premises, including GP premises that had not been subject to CHC examination, and will also be able to nominate a member to the trust board. A new national Commission for Patient and Public Involvement will support public involvement activities locally. Patients have also been given a say on national regulatory bodies and on the new National Institute for Clinical Excellence.

Proposed structures for public and patient involvement, 2001

- Statutory *patients' forums* to inspect services at NHS trust level (including in each PCT) – functions to include electing a member to the board, monitoring service quality, overseeing Patient Advice and Liaison Services (PALS), making reports on trust activities, and inspecting services without notice.
- A national *Commission for Patient and Public Involvement in Health* (CPPIH)– to set standards for patient involvement, represent patients' views in NHS policy-making, commission research, report to the Commission for Health Improvement and provide training for public representatives in the NHS.
- Local networks, reporting to the CPPIH to support community involvement in health services and to work with local Patients' Forums.
- *Local authority overview and scrutiny committees* with a remit to scrutinise local health services.

Source: *Involving Patients and the Public in Health care: Response to the listening exercise*, London: Department of Health, 2002

Some key areas have still to be tackled. Involving communities in making difficult decisions about service reconfigurations – most contentiously, the closure or downgrading of hospitals – is an important area where little progress has been made since 1997. The Government made a commitment in *The New NHS* to issue guidance on how to work with local communities on reconfiguration. Although a new National Independent Panel has been set up to provide advice on contested plans, guidance to help trusts set up transparent processes to work with their local communities on major service reconfigurations and hospital closures has not yet been forthcoming.

Equally, the Government has not yet put in place a new complaints system, as promised in *The New NHS*. Its 1999 review of the existing complaints procedure showed that the system was not working well: 50 per cent of people who had used the system thought their complaint was handled badly. On the basis on the review, the Government drew up a set of proposals, including uniform processes for independent review panels across the country, greater use of independent conciliation services and quarterly reporting of complaints to trust boards. Its listening exercise concluded in October 2001 and announced that the reformed complaints system would be implemented 'by 2002 at the very latest'.[13] Six months on, it is not yet clear how the new system will operate and how it will link into other measures, particularly the new Patient Advice and Liaison Services, which aim to resolve patients' problems before they reach formal complaints.

The impact of policy

Public information – reflecting the public's priorities?

Despite the range of initiatives that have been put in place to give the public more access to data about health services, little is known about the public's reaction to this information or whether patients are using information to help make decisions about local services.

More fundamentally, it is not clear whether the measures set out in the National Performance Assessment Framework reflect the public's main priorities. The NPAF was drawn up without input from either the wider public or organisations representing them. Complaints data suggest that the issues that the public is most likely to complain about are not always the areas monitored through the NPAF (*see* Figure 25). Specific complaints about staff attitudes and cancelled outpatients appointments are among the most common complaints against NHS organisations, yet neither are recorded in the NPAF.

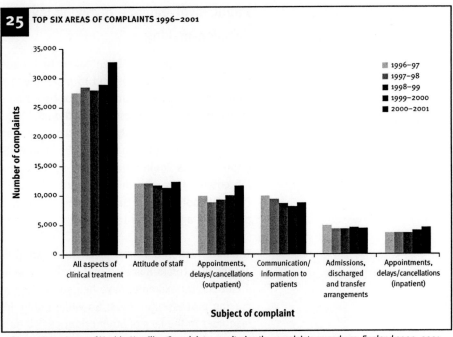

25 TOP SIX AREAS OF COMPLAINTS 1996–2001

Source: Department of Health. *Handling Complaints: monitoring the complaints procedures. England 2000–2001* (www.doh.gov.uk/nhscomplaints/bground.html)

Lay members have helped to bring a new perspective into the decision-making processes of PCGs.

Patient choice – are new services reaching those who need them most?

During the Government's first five years, increasing effort was put into extending patient choice and attempting to make services more responsive to local need. It is still too early to assess the full impact of these initiatives, scheduled to come on line within the ten-year period set out in *The NHS Plan*. Evaluations of schemes such as NHS Direct and walk-in centres are showing some early signs of success, offering greater flexibility in the way patients get access to advice and primary care services. Satisfaction rates with first-wave NHS Direct pilots have been high[14] and the service has helped to reduce anxiety about symptoms, as well as directing callers to the appropriate services.[15] Walk-in centres have given patients greater flexibility about when they are seen and longer consultations with staff. However, these early evaluations only reveal a limited picture of performance in certain parts of the country and do not necessarily reflect an accurate picture of the situation nationally.

Doubts remain about whether these new services are reaching people in greatest need. Although some walk-in centres are treating a high per centage of people who are not currently registered with GPs,[16] levels of awareness about NHS Direct may be lowest among groups most vulnerable to ill health. One study found that people over 65, from ethnic minorities or from less affluent areas were least likely to be aware of the service.[17]

The Government's promise to give patients greater choice over the location of their treatment has had some early results. Within a month of announcing that patients who had been waiting longer than 28 weeks could be treated at another hospital, 10 patients had made the trip to Lille in France for treatment, paid for by the NHS. But data about the costs of offering treatment abroad has not been made available and it is not clear whether the private sector and hospitals abroad are offering reduced-price treatment as a loss-leader to bring in higher volumes further down the line. The debate about choice over treatment has been largely divorced from a wider debate about the costs to the NHS as a whole of expanding choice.

Public involvement – involving lay members and patients in NHS decision-making

Significant steps have been taken to broaden the range of people taking up positions on NHS boards and to make these people more representative of local communities. New requirements for board members to live locally have been one important sign of progress, and, although the level of representation by women and ethnic minorities has only shifted slightly under Labour, there has been an increase in the proportion of both groups who chair NHS trusts.[18] The new independent NHS Appointments Commission, which sets out clear selection processes and uniform job criteria, may also help to tackle charges, confirmed by the Commissioner for Public Appointments, Dame Rennie Fritchie, that appointments were becoming politicised again under Labour.[19]

The introduction of formal mechanisms for public involvement within primary care groups and trusts has also had positive results in some parts of the country. Lay members, for example, have helped to bring a new perspective into the decision-making processes of PCGs. So while public involvement has fought for time and resources in the face of other priorities,[20] it has helped to deliver a range of service improvements for local people, including improving knowledge about health service systems and processes, and giving people more confidence in dealing with health professionals.[21]

It is still too early to assess the impact of some of the measures outlined in *The NHS Plan* to increase patient and public involvement. Many, such as Patients' Forums, the Commission for Patient and Public Involvement, and the new role for local authority overview and scrutiny committees, have not yet been put in place. Others, such as Patient Advice and Liaison Services (PALS) – set up to act as learning sites for the rest of the country – are just starting up. Anecdotal evidence from some of the early PALS suggests that the service is being well-used, although in some areas many of the queries are coming from NHS staff rather than patients.

Delays introducing the new complaints system have meant that performance against national targets has shown a decline under Labour. The number of complaints has risen significantly (*see* Figure 26) and the number resolved within the target time has fallen from 66.7 per cent in 1996–97 to 55.6 per cent in 2000–01.[22] The Government's principal aim has been to set up the new PALS to deal with difficulties before they reach formal complaints but the links between this service and the complaints system have not been clearly articulated.

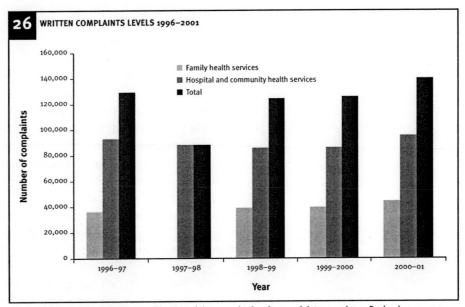

26 WRITTEN COMPLAINTS LEVELS 1996–2001

Source: Department of Health. *Handling Complaints: monitoring the complaints procedures. England 2000–2001* (www.doh.gov.uk/nhscomplaints/bground.html)

Conclusions

Public information and patient choice – an ideological or pragmatic choice?

Although the Government's attempts to make more information about NHS performance available to the public are important steps forward, it is unclear whether ministers have a clear view about how and why the public should use this information. Whether this information is simply to inform the public, or to be used by the Department of Health to put pressure on the NHS to improve its performance, is unclear, though much of the rhetoric has focused on the latter objective.

There are signs that the Government would like patients to take an active approach to their health care, using performance data to influence choices about where they

The Government will have to consider how much real choice about different models of care should be offered to patients, and whether taxpayers will be prepared to fund this.

are treated. This is apparent in the introduction of Patients' Prospectuses, particularly in primary care – where the public will be able to use information about practice performance to select their GP – and also with the appointment of patient care advisors to help patients waiting beyond national targets times for heart surgery to assess different options.

But whether the public wants to exercise this degree of choice is unclear. In the case of secondary care, evidence from the first national survey of patients' views on general practice[23] showed that 75 percent were happy for their GPs to make a decision about where they should be referred to, and only 7 percent would like to have been given a choice. Although this may reflect low expectations among patients, it may also challenge the Government's assertions that, in a consumerist society, people expect a similar level of choice over their health care as over their car insurance or shopping.

Even the small proportion of patients who do want to make a choice over treatment are likely to find it hard to interpret the number of different systems for assessing and reviewing performance. United Bristol Health care – one of the so-called 'dirty dozen' trusts which failed to get a single star in September 2001 – was rated one of the highest performers for heart bypass surgery in a Dr Foster/*The Times* survey.[24] Simpler, standardised information will be needed if the public is able to use performance data in a meaningful way.

The rhetoric over choice has grown stronger during Labour's first five years in office. But whether ideology or pragmatism has motivated this is not clear. Many of the Government's initiatives in this area have focused on making existing services more responsive to people's needs (for example, extending opening times in primary care and the booked-admissions project). These initiatives give the public more choice over the time and, in some cases, the location of their treatment but do not offer any choice between different models of care. If initiatives to increase public involvement in local service planning work effectively, the Government is likely to come under increasing public pressure to offer real choice about alternative forms of service to patients. This is far from being a reality at the moment, except in limited areas, for example, maternity services.

Equally, the reasons for offering patients on long waiting lists the choice of treatment in another hospital, the private sector or abroad seems primarily to be pragmatic, motivated by the need to reduce waiting times. Again, these schemes offer limited choice: wait longer and be treated locally or travel for treatment and be dealt with more quickly.

The Government will have to face up to some key dilemmas over the extent to which choice will become a reality in the NHS. Treating patients abroad has raised the question of how much taxpayers are prepared to spend to reduce waiting lists and how to make the necessary trade-off between reducing waiting times and increased expenditure. In the longer term, the Government will also have to consider how much real choice about different models of care should be offered to patients, and whether taxpayers will be prepared to fund this.

Public involvement – reconciling local choice with national equity

Many of the measures that the Government has introduced to increase patient and public involvement are real steps forward. Patients' Forums will give patients greater access to senior decision-makers in trusts. Used constructively, the new scrutiny function could be a powerful tool for engaging communities in a face-to-face discussion with local health services about local priorities and the effectiveness of services. Requirements on primary care trusts to consult with local people have begun to increase the NHS's capacity to engage with the communities they serve.

But the Government made a series of blunders that called into question whether their commitment to greater public involvement at all levels was genuine. First, public involvement in setting *NHS Plan* priorities was weak. Patients and the wider public were included in discussions about their priorities for the health service through a hastily compiled leaflet, only available in English, which asked the public for their top three priorities for the NHS. Just 151,999 responses were received to the 12 million produced, with the majority coming from people aged between 45 and 64.[25] With two weeks for the public to send in their views and 10 days for these to be worked into the Plan, the exercise did not inspire confidence that the Government was committed to making the NHS more transparent and responsive to the public.[26]

Second, the Government's treatment of community health councils (CHCs) was crude. Without prior warning or consultation, *The NHS Plan* announced the abolition of CHCs. This became an unexpected battleground in the Commons. Many of the proposals designed to increase patient and public involvement in the NHS became hostages to Parliamentary time and were dropped from the Health and Social Care Act after wrangling in both Houses and demonstrations outside the Palace of Westminster. Critics argued that this was another sign of a Government that found dealing with criticism tough, by trying to replace outspoken CHCs with more pliable NHS-based structures. They pointed to work such as Casualty Watch, the pan-London monthly survey of A&E waiting times carried out by a consortium of CHCs which often made uncomfortable reading for ministers and NHS managers – a clear challenge to New Labour's assertions that it was bringing the NHS out of the doldrums.

Although the new Junior Health Minister, Hazel Blears (herself a former CHC chair) embarked upon a nationwide 'listening exercise' to consult on the new patient involvement proposals – and modified the new structures to reflect concerns about their feasibility – the Government has refused to back down on the abolition of CHCs and has rejected calls to transform them into new Patients' Councils. This has alienated many of Labour's natural allies in its drive to increase patient and public involvement, including national and local patients' organisations whose support will be crucial to the success of the new patient and public involvement structures.

More fundamentally, the public's capacity to influence service planning and prioritisation at a more strategic level – for example, by expressing their view on local HIMPs – is constrained by national performance management systems. The Government has made it very clear that trusts must deliver against key national targets or ultimately face sanctions such as the imposition of franchised management teams. If the Government is serious about genuine public involvement, trusts should be allowed to choose their own priorities where there is a clear rationale and strong community support. The problem facing Labour is how to reconcile greater local choice with national equity. Although the devolution of funding to PCTs has signaled a clear desire to devolve responsibility to local levels, unless performance management systems are made more accommodating of local need, the public's capacity to influence local services will be limited to endorsing nationally-set priorities.

The bigger picture

Labour came to power promising a more open, accountable and responsive NHS in which the public had a greater say over the services they received. Throughout Labour's first five years, the political rhetoric around this principle has grown louder. The 1997 manifesto simply promised greater local representation on NHS trust boards. By 2001, individual patients were to be given more choice about services and more power in decision-making about their own treatment. They would be able to influence local service provision through representation on Patient's Forums and take part in consultation exercises about local service priorities. PALS would mean that where patients or their relatives were not satisfied with their care, problems would be resolved speedily. Finally, they could add their views about the effectiveness of local services by contributing to Commission for Health Improvement reviews, local Patients' Surveys and local council overview and scrutiny committees.

On the ground, the picture remains confused. Although the new structures are beginning to offer more opportunities for the public to influence local health services and to access services conveniently, it is uncertain how radical the Government is prepared to be and how much control they are prepared to cede.

Real patient choice over services remains marginal although more effort has gone into making services more responsive to local need. The full impact of these changes will not be clear for some time, and it also remains to be seen how far the Government is prepared to support (and the public to endorse) real choice over different models of care. The language of choice appears to be primarily targeted at increasing capacity to deliver against key targets rather than representing a more fundamental shift in ideology.

The verdict

Emerging policies on patient and public involvement suggest a significant change in the culture of the NHS. While the impact to date has been limited, the Government's promotion of enhanced patient choice may begin to knock down the paternalism that has characterised much of the NHS to date.

11 Health inequalities

Key issues:

- Putting inequalities on the policy map
- New Deals and other Treasury-led initiatives
- Health Action Zones and other area-based programmes
- 'Saving Lives' and health inequalities targets
- Health-related changes since 1997

The inheritance

A widening health gap

In 1997, the 'health gap' between rich and poor was equivalent to nine years of life. A boy born into the poorest social group (class V) was likely to live for 68.2 years, compared with 77.7 years for a boy in the richest social group (class I). For women, the gap was 6.4 years. This gap had widened over the previous 20 years, by four years for men and 1.1 years for women.[1]

Inequalities in Health,[2] commissioned by the Callaghan Government in 1977, was published after Margaret Thatcher became Prime Minister in 1980. *The Black Report*, as it became known, clearly identified health inequalities and the links with factors such as income, education and employment. However, its recommendations were considered too costly and out of step with the political ideology of the four Conservative administrations between 1979 and 1997. They were never implemented.

According to the neo-liberal ideology that shaped policy for much of that period, the priority for the Government was to roll back the state and free the market. This would lead to more enterprise and wealth creation. Wealth would 'trickle down' to the poor and socially disadvantaged. Aside from that, the route to good health was primarily a matter of personal responsibility and lifestyle choices – not a matter for government intervention.

Positive steps

Two positive steps were taken during the Conservative years. *The Health of the Nation,* published in 1992,[3] was the first major public health policy document to be published by a UK Government. It made several references to health variations between occupational and ethnic groups, as well as between the north and south of the country. However, these were attributed to lifestyle and (unexplained) inequalities in access to service, rather than to socio-economic factors. The second step was to make an unprecedented investment in research that would deepen and refine understanding of the extent and causes of health inequalities. Consequently, a great deal more was known about health inequalities by 1997 than under previous administrations.

The Government promised a 'third way between the old extremes of individual victim-blaming on the one hand and nanny state social engineering on the other'.

The policy pledges

New goals for improving health

New Labour promised in its 1997 manifesto that a new minister for public health would 'attack the root causes of ill health, and so improve lives and save the NHS money'. It pledged to 'set new goals for improving the overall health of the nation' that would 'recognise the impact that poverty, poor housing, unemployment and a polluted environment have on health.' Additionally, to prevent illness, Labour pledged to ban tobacco advertising and to establish an independent Food Standards Agency.

Assessing health inequalities

Labour's first significant step in Government was to bring *The Black Report* up to date: in 1997, it commissioned an independent inquiry into health inequalities, chaired by former Chief Medical Officer Sir Donald Acheson. Its brief was to summarise evidence, spot trends, and identify priority areas for future developments likely to lead to 'beneficial, cost effective and affordable interventions to reduce health inequalities'. Acheson reported on the inquiry's findings in November 1998,[4] with 39 recommendations and four headline priorities:

- All policies likely to have a direct or indirect effect on health should be evaluated for their impact on health inequalities.
- All those policies should be formulated to favour the less well-off.
- Priority should be given to the health of women of child-bearing age, expectant mothers and young children.
- Further steps should be taken to reduce income inequalities and improve the living standards of poor households.

A 'third way' to health improvement

The Government's first public health Green Paper, *Our Healthier Nation* (1998),[5] pledged to 'improve the health of the population as a whole by increasing the length of people's lives and the number of years people spend free from illness' and to 'improve the health of the worst off in society and to narrow the health gap'. It acknowledged that there were sound economic reasons for improving health – citing days off work for illness and demands on the NHS – and promised a 'third way between the old extremes of individual victim-blaming on the one hand and nanny state social engineering on the other'. The Green Paper identified four targets to reduce premature deaths: cancer, coronary heart disease and stroke, accidents and mental health. Those targets would be met though a 'contract' between individuals, local communities and national government, working in three settings – healthy workplaces, healthy schools and healthy neighbourhoods.

Disease-based targets

The White Paper that followed in 1999, *Saving Lives: Our healthier nation,*[6] was much more narrowly focused on NHS-related measures intended to meet the four targets, with numbers (of deaths to be avoided) and dates specified. It claimed that the Government was addressing inequality 'with a range of initiatives on education, welfare-to-work, housing, neighbourhoods, transport and the environment which will help improve health.' This was fleshed out by the formal response to the Acheson Report, published on the same day.[7] Here it laid claim to 'the most comprehensive programme of work to tackle health inequalities ever undertaken in this country'. In effect, this was a summary of most aspects of the social and economic policies being pursued across Government.

A year later, Labour's interim report [8] outlining progress during its first three years in office renewed the promise 'to close the gap between the worst off and the better off' promising to intervene 'sooner rather than later' in 'transforming the NHS from a service that does not just fix and mend the ill, but which prevents and protects against illness'.

The Government's actions

There has been no shortage of measures to address health inequalities since 1997. Here we focus on four categories of initiative: those led by the Treasury, area-based programmes, target-driven initiatives and measures focused on the NHS.

Treasury-led initiatives

From 1997 onwards, there has been a steady flow of measures intended to reduce dependency on welfare benefits and increase the numbers in paid work. The main focus has been on making families with young children more self-sufficient and better off, and on helping to pursue the ambitious goal of eliminating child poverty by 2020. The 'new deals' for lone parents, for young unemployed people and for those out of work for two years or more, were later extended to all unemployed people, including disabled people. The minimum wage (£3.60 in 1999, going up to £4.20 in 2002 for those 22 years old or over) helped to make work more attractive in financial terms, as did the working families tax credit, introduced in October 1999 to top up low wages for those with families to support. There were also significant increases in income support for non-working families and in child benefit (from £14.40 to £15.50 per week for the eldest child), as well as a substantial investment (£66 million for 2000/01) in a new national childcare strategy, to remove the most significant barrier to parents entering paid work. As these measures came on stream, they coincided with a four-year economic boom between 1997 and 2001, during which time the unemployment rate fell from 7.1 to 4.8 per cent.

In 2001, the Treasury instigated a cross-cutting review of spending on health inequalities. This is claimed as a unique opportunity to examine the impact on health inequalities of spending across Government departments and is expected to recommend ways of improving the use of existing resources, and encouraging an integrated approach to health inequalities and more effective cross-Government working. A key sector, for example, is education, where spending on efforts to raise standards of education and improve schools in disadvantaged areas has doubled since 1997.

Area-based initiatives

Since 1998/9, every health authority has been obliged to produce a Health Improvement Plan (later to become a Health Improvement and Modernisation Plan, or HIMP), in partnership with local authorities and other local private, voluntary and statutory organisations, which will 'modernise services to tackle ill health, as well as the root causes of ill health',[9] and reduce variations in service provision. Local authorities, for their part, are expected to develop their own Community Plans, also in partnership with other local bodies, for improving services and promoting well-being and a better quality of life.

Health Action Zones

Twenty-six Health Action Zones were set up between 1998 and 2001, covering 13 million people in 34 health authorities and 73 local authorities. Health Action Zones, along with Education and Employment Action Zones, were early attempts by Labour to tackle disadvantage by loosening red tape and encouraging innovation. Investment in HAZs has been relatively modest, with £320 million made available for three years from 1999. HAZs are expected to come up with their own ideas and have the freedom to implement them. They are guided by seven principles, the first of which is 'reducing health inequalities, promoting equality of access to services and improving equity in resource allocation'. They are also intended to engage communities, work in partnership, engage frontline staff, and take a 'whole systems' approach that is evidence based and 'person-centred'.[10]

A wide range of innovative projects has been launched in designated Health Action Zones, with varying degrees of success. In Bury and Rochdale, for example, a new Action against Asthma campaign aims to achieve large reductions in the area's high rates of hospital re-admission and visits by children to A&E departments. It centres on home visits by a specialist asthma nurse and an environmental health officer, followed up by a health visitor, and backed by an efficient interpreting and translation support service. In Luton, Bedfordshire, a project to improve the quality of private sector housing for older and disabled people brings together health and housing professionals to identify needs and speed up renovations. In Hackney, East London, pregnant women and vulnerable mothers under 21 receive mentoring and support from other young mothers. Community participation and development, social inclusion, employment and child health are all themes that feature strongly in the HAZs' portfolio of activities.[11]

Healthy Living Centres

In a parallel move, £300 million was made available from the National Lottery's New Opportunities Fund to set up Healthy Living Centres in disadvantaged areas, charged with addressing inequalities, supporting local health aims and involving the community in measures to help improve health locally. Altogether, 136 grants had been awarded to Healthy Living Centres by the end of 2001.

Sure Start

Sure Start, another area-based initiative, was set up in 1998 under the auspices of the Minister for Public Health, to improve the life chances of very young children in deprived areas by making sure they are ready to learn when they reach school age. Up to 250 neighbourhood-level programmes, combining health, education and social services, are intended to support 18 per cent of poor children under four. Funds have increased from £184 million in 2000–01 to £499 million by 2003–04, to enable the programme to almost double its reach by 2004. Sure Start aims to reduce the numbers on the child protection register, the number of mothers smoking in pregnancy, the proportion of children with speech and language problems requiring specialist intervention. It also aims to help reduce the number of 0–3-year-olds living in households where no-one is employed, for example, by directing unemployed parents towards welfare-to-work programmes.

In *The NHS Plan*, published in 2000, the Government announced that new national targets would be introduced to reduce health inequalities – these key targets addressed infant mortality and adult life expectancy.

New Deal for Communities

The New Deal for Communities, launched in 1998, is intended to tackle multiple deprivation in the poorest neighbourhoods in the country, giving them resources to tackle their problems in an intensive and co-ordinated way. In each case, a community-based partnership must tackle poor health as well as poor job prospects, high levels of crime, educational under-achievement, and problems with housing and the physical environment. Over £1.9 billion has been committed to 39 NDC partnerships.

Many of these area-based initiatives and structures overlap, creating some confusion at local level. In 2000 the Treasury carried out a review of Government Interventions in Deprived Areas (GIDA),[12] which marked an important shift away from ad-hoc spending on additional programmes, towards an overhaul of mainstream government activity. In future, the review said, 'core public services like schools and the police should be equipped to become the main weapons against deprivation'. Public Service Agreements – a central mechanism for monitoring the performance of Government departments – were to include targets for reducing inequalities in education, employment, crime levels and social housing for the first time.

Local Strategic Partnerships

In 2001 a new model – Local Strategic Partnerships (LSPs) – was introduced, initially for 88 local authority areas receiving Neighbourhood Renewal Funds. LSPs are expected to co-ordinate local initiatives and funding, bringing together a wide range of people to work together on inter-linked issues such as health, housing and the environment. They aim to promote joint working in order to 'improve all public services; renew deprived areas; develop strong, sustainable economies and healthy, safe communities'.[13]

Target-driven initiatives

The 1999 public health White Paper, *Saving Lives: Our healthier nation*, set out specific targets: by 2010 to reduce the number of premature deaths per year from cancer by 100,000, from coronary heart disease and stroke by 200,000, from accidents by 12,000 and from suicide by 4,000. According to the Government's response to the Acheson Report,[14] these were 'to be matched by tough local inequalities targets, reflecting the different aspects and varied extent of inequality across the country.' The mechanism for achieving this was to be health improvement programmes (*see* above).

In 2001, the Health Development Agency produced guidance[15] on developing local targets for tackling health inequalities. It cited a wide variety of practical examples drawn from health improvement programmes and Health Action Zones. These range from 'creating 10 community champions and declaring one healthy neighbourhood in 2000/2001' (Wigan) and 'ensuring over a 10-year period that all residents have access to affordable, good quality food' (Stockport) to 'improving access by siting a mobile mammography unit in areas of low uptake' (Lambeth, Southwark and Lewisham).

In *The NHS Plan,* published in 2000, the Government announced[16] that new national targets would be introduced to reduce health inequalities. These key targets addressed infant mortality and adult life expectancy, and were set out in a consultation document:[17]

- For children under one year, to reduce the gap in mortality between manual groups and the population as a whole by at least 10 per cent by 2010.
- For health authorities, to reduce the gap between the fifth of areas with the lowest life expectancy and the population as a whole by at least 10 per cent by 2010.

The consultation document pointed out that three other existing targets also impacted on health inequalities:

- To reduce the number of children living in poverty by a quarter by 2004 and eradicate child poverty by 2010.
- To reduce smoking rates among manual groups from 32 per cent in 1998 to 26 per cent in 2010.
- To reduce under-18 conceptions by 15 per cent by 2004 and by 50 per cent by 2010, while reducing the gap in rates between the worst fifth of wards and the average by at least a quarter.

The key mechanisms for delivering on the inequalities targets were identified as primary care trusts (PCTs) and local strategic partnerships. An Inequalities and Public Health Task Force was set up at national level, as well as one in each region, as part of a new network of task forces to help implement *The NHS Plan*. The Treasury's cross-cutting review is expected to inform the way government departments contribute to reducing health inequalities. A delivery plan, setting out measures intended to meet the targets, is due out in the summer of 2002.

More specifically, the *National Service Framework for Coronary Heart Disease* (2000)[18] – designed to focus resources and prioritise action within the NHS – focused on reducing inequalities as a key theme, which involved 'ensuring that less well advanced organisations, including those which may face particular challenges or difficult circumstances, are able to learn from the experience of those which have made more rapid progress, and are given appropriate support'. *The Cancer Plan* (2000)[19] has four aims, one of which is 'to tackle the inequalities in health that mean unskilled workers are twice as likely to die from cancer as professionals'. Measures to achieve this include smoking cessation schemes aimed at low-income groups and schemes to improve nutrition – free fruit for primary school children, and a 'Five a Day' campaign to encourage people to eat more fruit and vegetables.

Improving access to health services

Health improvement, including reducing health inequalities, and 'fair access' to health services according to need, are among six goals defining the Performance Assessment Framework for the NHS. The framework is intended to ensure that universal standards are applied across the NHS and that low-income and socially-excluded groups and localities are not doubly disadvantaged by also having poorer quality health services. The National Service Frameworks (including those for coronary heart disease and cancer) help to set the parameters for performance assessment.

A review of NHS resource allocation was set up in 1998 with the main aim of contributing to 'a reduction in avoidable health inequalities'.[20] As a result, a new 'Health Inequalities Adjustment' has shifted the basis of allocation from securing equal opportunity of access to patients in equal need, towards positive action in favour of deprived areas. In 2001/2, the 47 health authorities judged to have the highest rates of 'avoidable mortality' received an additional £70 million, while a

The most striking increase in income between 1997 and 2000 has been among low-earning women and can be attributed largely to the minimum wage.

further £60 million went to Health Action Zones. This small addition to the £37 billion distributed to health authorities on the traditional 'equity of access' criterion might be expected to fund such NHS interventions as: increased levels of treatment for targeted populations; different and earlier treatment; greater efforts to secure patient compliance; targeted health promotion measures; improved co-ordination of other relevant agencies; and more effective collection and analysis of health data.[21]

At a local level, primary care trusts have a key role to play in reducing health inequalities through improved access to higher quality and more appropriate health services, as well as by participating in local strategic partnerships and regeneration schemes. Measures introduced since 1997 that might improve their capacity to reduce inequalities include:

- devolution of power to primary care trusts to enable them to tailor services to local needs
- New Personal Medical Services (PMS) contracts to employ salaried clinical staff in areas where it has been hard to recruit and retain GPs, especially deprived inner cities
- a new public health role for PCTs, giving them responsibility for population health
- involvement in drawing up and implementing Health Improvement and Modernisation Plans, local strategic partnerships and other area-based initiatives.

The impact of policy

One major change since 1997 is that health inequalities are now clearly on the policy map. The nature and extent of health inequalities, and their underlying social and economic causes, are widely acknowledged among policy-makers and practitioners in the field. It is broadly accepted that the problem requires urgent attention and that action must be taken across sectors and departments, not just by the NHS.

It is also widely understood that health inequalities are deeply entrenched and that progress towards reducing them is likely to be slow. It is necessary to monitor trends in underlying causes of health, such as income, employment and education, as well as behavioural factors such as smoking, and illness and death rates. What changes, if any, can be detected since 1997? Below we consider indications in population data.

Income and poverty

Unemployment, financial insecurity and poverty are all significant determinants of health. Thus measures to reduce welfare dependency and increase paid employment – if successfully implemented – can be expected to have a positive impact on health. The most striking increase in income between 1997 and 2000 has been among low-earning women and can be attributed largely to the minimum wage. Earnings of the lowest-paid women workers rose by 18.5 per cent, compared with a 12.7 per cent median increase. But the gap between male and female earnings remains wide: the median gross weekly earnings for women in 2000 were £93 less than men's.[22]

Between 1997 and 2000, the number of households below the 'poverty line' (measured as 60 per cent of median income) fell by 600,000 and the numbers of children in such households fell by 300,000, from 4.4 to 4.1 million.[23] Such figures are open to interpretation. The Government claimed to have lifted 1.2 million

Unemployment among young adults remains high and has increased slightly: it now stands at 10 per cent.

children out of poverty by the end of the last Parliament (June 2001) – a figure said to include those who would have been in poverty had it not been for the policies introduced by Labour.[24]

Education

The number of 11-year-olds achieving level 4 at Key Stage 2 rose between 1996 and 2000: from 52 to 75 per cent for English and from 54 to 72 per cent for Maths. If this can be sustained, it will meet the target set for 2002. Progress is slower for GCSE grades, where there has been an increase in students getting five or more A* to C grades from 42.5 per cent in 1997 to 47 per cent in 2000 – well below the target of 75 per cent by 2004. Improvement has been much greater among manual groups than among non-manual groups.[25]

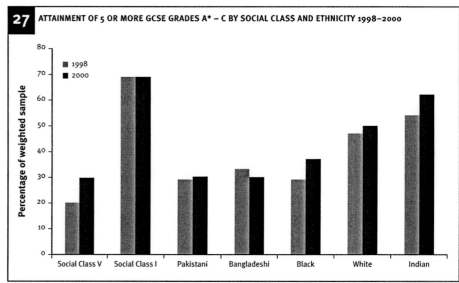

27 ATTAINMENT OF 5 OR MORE GCSE GRADES A* – C BY SOCIAL CLASS AND ETHNICITY 1998–2000

Source: Youth Cohort Study, ONS, 2001

Black and Indian students have improved their educational performance more than white and Pakistani students, while Bangladeshis' performance has declined. The gap between Inner and Outer London has widened slightly. The proportion of students achieving five or more A starred to C grades at GCSE increased between 1997 and 2000 by 5.1 per cent in Outer London and by 3.7 per cent in Inner London.[26]

Employment

Unemployment has fallen from 7.1 per cent in 1997 to 4.8 per cent in 2001. Currently there are 3.5 million adults who would like to have paid work but do not. Unemployment among young adults remains high and has increased slightly: it now stands at 10 per cent.[27] There has been no discernible improvement in rates of long-term employment, with 1.8 million out of work for three years or more in 1997 and 2001.[28]

Smoking, teenage pregnancy and obesity

Self-reported smoking rates have declined since the mid-1970s, but have levelled off recently. Smoking rates remain much higher among manual than non-manual groups, although the gap is narrowing slightly. Between 1998 and 2000, smoking decreased among manual men and women (by 2 and 1 per cent respectively).

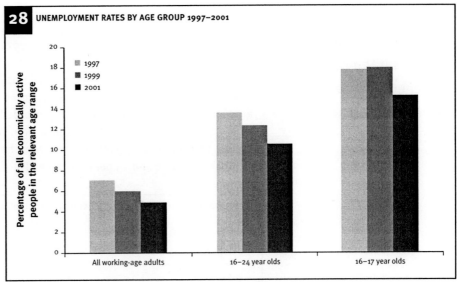

Source: Labour Force Survey, ONS, 2001

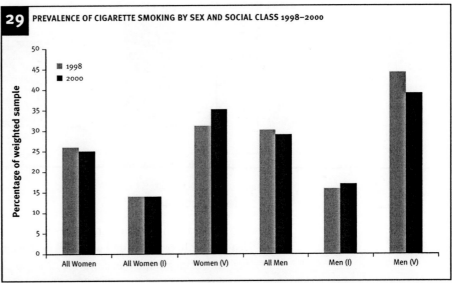

Source: Living in Britain, ONS, 2000

However, smoking among *unskilled* manual women increased by four per cent over that period. In 2000, 4 per cent of women in social class I reported smoking while pregnant, compared with 26 per cent in social class V.[29]

The numbers of births to girls conceiving before the age of 16 has fallen by 20 per cent since 1996, but the vast majority of these births are concentrated in the manual social classes and the rate of teenage conception in the UK remains higher than elsewhere in Western Europe. Rates in Scotland are higher than in the rest of the UK.[30]

Obesity levels have risen between 1997 and 2000, by 4 per cent for men and 1.7 per cent for women. There has been no change in numbers of men and women who are considered overweight, remaining at 44.5 per cent of men and 33.8 per cent of women in 2000.[31]

Infant mortality rates fell between 1997 and 2000, but the gap has widened between the lowest and highest social groups.

Infant mortality

Overall, infant mortality rates fell between 1997 and 2000, but the gap has widened between the lowest and highest social groups. Between 1997–9 and 1998–2000, there was a decline of 5.8 per cent in social class I and a rise of 2.9 per cent in social class V, so that the rate for the poorest is now double that for the wealthiest. Rates are higher for infants whose birth was recorded solely by the mother (38 per cent higher than the overall rate), for those born to mothers under 20 (50 per cent higher) and for those whose mothers were born in Pakistan and the Caribbean (more than double and 93 per cent respectively).[32]

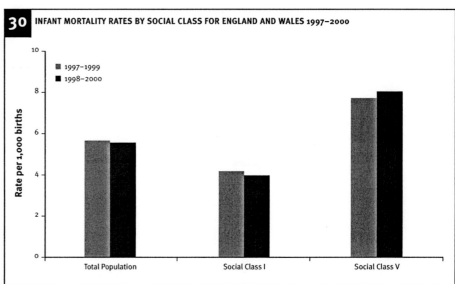

30 INFANT MORTALITY RATES BY SOCIAL CLASS FOR ENGLAND AND WALES 1997–2000

Source: London Health Observatory, 2001

Life expectancy

Life expectancy in England and Wales has increased between 1996 and 1999 (by 1.1 years at birth for males and 0.4 years for females). The gap between the lowest and highest social groups has narrowed. But the picture is mixed: for example, men in social class II have improved their life expectancy by 1.6 years more than men in social class IV and men in the highest group can still expect to live seven years longer than men in the lowest group. There remain marked inequalities between ethnic groups, between men and women and between the north and south of the UK. Life expectancy in Scotland is 72.8 years for men compared with 75 years in England and Wales. The number of women dying at childbirth doubled in Scotland between 1997 and 2000, remaining steady in England and Wales.[33]

Death rates in England have decreased for heart disease, stroke and cancer, but not disproportionately for lower social groups. There has been no improvement in deaths caused by accidents, and suicide rates have increased.[34]

Conclusions

In 1997, New Labour stepped into a field where evidence and understanding of health inequalities were highly developed, where the case for intervention was strong, but where there were no recent precedents for Government action. Tackling health inequalities chimed well with New Labour's identity. Though the Labour Government sought to distance itself from traditional leftist redistribution and 'nanny statism', it needed to project a strong commitment to social justice and

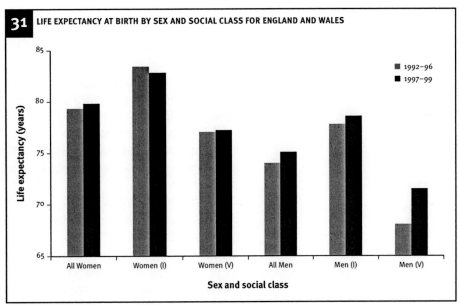

31 LIFE EXPECTANCY AT BIRTH BY SEX AND SOCIAL CLASS FOR ENGLAND AND WALES

Source: ONS, 2002

equal opportunity – both to distinguish itself from its predecessor and to protect its left flank. As it repositioned itself in the centre of the political spectrum, New Labour would be more comfortable taking a stand against health inequalities than owning up to income redistribution. Many of the same measures were needed to address both – so the idea of equal health chances could operate as a proxy for social and economic equality without raising the ghosts of 'old Labour'.

Changing the climate of opinion

A major achievement of the new Government was to change the climate of opinion. It put health inequalities firmly on the policy agenda, changed the language and helped to build a new consensus acknowledging the nature and urgency of the problem, its causes and ways that it could be addressed. Labour also rehabilitated two concepts that are now widely recognised as essential to tackling health inequalities: locally-based partnerships that cross old boundaries, and community development. It is impossible to measure the impact of these shifts in 'received wisdom', but they were real and significant – creating a sound basis for action. The Government has not yet delivered on its promise of a total ban on tobacco advertising, but it has fulfilled its manifesto pledge to establish a Food Standards Agency.

Investing in anti-poverty measures

Labour's high-profile efforts to combat social exclusion, to move more people off benefits and into paid work, and to end child poverty, appear to have yielded some tangible results. Unemployment and child poverty are down; low earners have increased their earnings disproportionately; and GCSE results are improving, especially among lower-income groups. Cynics may attribute these developments to a sustained global economic boom, to creative statistical analysis, or to a dilution of educational standards. However, the fact remains that the Government has made a heavy investment – in terms of resources and political capital – and has applied itself energetically to a range of tasks that are intended to pursue these objectives. Most measures introduced since 1997 cannot realistically be expected to yield verifiable results for at least another five years.

Developing area-based initiatives

Area-based interventions are even more difficult to assess. Sure Start is almost universally regarded as a promising initiative, although it is too early to measure outcomes. It focuses on young children in disadvantaged areas and is based on evidence that positive pre-school experience can lead to improved health and opportunities later on. The Neighbourhood Renewal Strategy, with its recent emphasis on shifting mainstream budgets and programmes to deliver local change, marks a move away from unsustainable ad-hoc initiatives while addressing the immediate and longer-term needs of poor neighbourhoods.

Health improvement and modernisation plans (HIMPs) have received mixed notices. The idea of local cross-sectoral partnerships developing plans to improve health and reduce health inequalities was broadly welcomed on all sides. But several factors have conspired to limit their effectiveness. Reorganisation of the health sector at primary care level has absorbed time, energy and attention that might otherwise have been spent developing HIMPs. Forming useful partnerships is especially difficult while one partner is in a state of constant upheaval. The planning process has been confused by a lack of clarity over how HIMPs should relate to the local authorities' Community Plans. The centrally-imposed imperatives of cutting waiting lists and 'saving lives' threatened by the 'big killers' (heart disease, stroke and cancer) have limited the extent to which HIMPs can innovate to improve health, or identify and address the underlying causes of local health inequalities.

As for Health Action Zones, it took longer than anticipated for them to form productive local partnerships, to develop viable projects and to spend the money allocated. They were afflicted by – and contributed to – confusion caused by a plethora of area-based initiatives, many covering similar ground. The HAZs are due to be wound up earlier than originally planned, and it is expected that some of their activities will come under the auspices of local strategic partnerships.

Inequalities targets

Designing a health policy agenda around specific targets, to be measured in terms of health outcomes, is a risky business. Mortality statistics are harder to manipulate than figures on child poverty. On one hand, targets provide a strong sense of direction and purpose and can be easily understood. On the other, they can lead to over-simplification and even to distorted priorities. Actions whose impact cannot be measured by avoidable deaths may be sidelined, even if they are likely to improve health in the longer term. Resources may be focused too narrowly on areas where the Government feels confident of achieving measurable gains. Saving lives, especially by means of clinical treatment, is not the same as improving health so that treatment is not required. The 'big killer' targets are supposed to be supported by strategies to reduce inequalities, but it is the headline figures that dominate policy and practice, not the aim of reducing their unequal impact. It is too early to tell whether the revised resource allocation formula for the NHS will make any impact on health inequalities.

The introduction of national inequalities targets came late – more than two years after the announcement of disease-based targets. One effect has been to signal a kind of hierarchy. At the top are the disease-based targets for heart disease, stroke and cancer, backed up by detailed implementation plans and serious money. Next, mental health (suicides) and accidents, less well developed and resourced, but nevertheless part of the main 'saving lives' agenda. At the bottom are the health

Power follows money, and money follows the NHS.

inequalities targets, feeling like an afterthought, with some serious consideration and commitment behind them, but not much money, or much clout (yet). The Treasury's cross-cutting review on health inequalities and the Department of Health's forthcoming delivery plan are promising moves. Whether they are sufficient remains to be seen. A massive and sustained input of resources and political initiative is required to reverse trends in life expectancy and infant mortality, where the gap between richer and poorer social groups continues to widen.

Health inequalities are intrinsically hard to handle because they arise from complex and inter-related problems that cannot be solved solely by the NHS, or the Department of Health. They cry out for 'joined-up' Government, but this has been slow to develop and remains fraught with difficulties. The Government chose not to replicate its model for tackling social exclusion, which involved setting up a designated unit in the Cabinet Office reporting directly to the Prime Minister. It was hardly irrational to locate responsibility for health inequalities within the Department of Health and, by and large, the two Ministers for Public Health (Tessa Jowell and Yvette Cooper) have demonstrated strong commitment to the issue. But power follows money, and money follows the NHS. This influences explicit and implicit priority-setting throughout the organisation.

Health inequalities and the wider public health agenda are not as high as they might be on the Department's must-do list, for several reasons:

- They are wicked issues for the NHS – they don't lend themselves to clinical solutions. They are 'upstream' issues that can only be addressed by long-term policies: they seldom provide the 'quick wins' that governments find so alluring.
- The NHS, like many other public sector organisations, has an inward-looking, risk-averse culture that mitigates against productive partnership working and innovation.
- The NHS is under huge pressure to deliver on a host of other objectives, such as reducing waiting times.
- The Secretary of State for Health and the Prime Minister consistently signal to the public that the *big* health problem they are determined to solve is the 'crisis' in the NHS. This ratchets up media scrutiny and public anxiety, ensuring that the NHS remains a political A&E case, forever in need of intensive care. The fact that disadvantaged groups and communities get ill more often and make more demands on the NHS, thereby contributing to its tribulations, is seldom taken into account and exerts little influence over the balance of priorities in Government policy.

In summary, Labour has stimulated a substantial volume of local and neighbourhood-based activities aimed at strengthening communities, improving public services and enhancing the quality of life – all of which may help to narrow the 'health gap'. Much of the time, however, its efforts have suffered from a lack of definition and top-level leadership. It has allowed the media to set the health policy agenda and has become trapped by its own rhetoric. The more the Government promises to 'save' the NHS and signals that this is what it *really* cares about, the harder it becomes for it to capture the public imagination for a different agenda aimed at reducing inequalities, improving health and, ultimately, checking demands on the NHS that are triggered or exacerbated by social and economic factors. In spite of unprecedented levels of activity around the new targets, health inequalities still appear to be a second-order issue, liable to be elbowed out by the more pressing problems presented by a massive provider of treatment and care. That is potentially bad news for health, especially for those most likely to get ill and die young. It is ultimately bad news for the NHS as well. And it could prove embarrassing for a Government that pledged to improve the health of the poorest when it took office in 1997.

The verdict

The Government deserves credit for putting the 'health gap' on the policy map, but has allowed it to remain a second-order issue. It has instigated an impressive series of actions to improve health and health care for the poorest in society. To reduce health inequalities, however, it must reverse trends in the opposite direction. It is unrealistic to expect demonstrable progress at this stage. But without stronger political leadership and a higher priority given to measures aimed at reducing inequalities, the chances of significantly reducing health inequalities in the next decade are slim.

Endnotes

Chapter 1 – Introduction

1   Labour Party Manifesto. *New Labour: because Britain deserves better*. London: The Labour Party, 1997.

2   Department of Health. *Working for Patients*. London: The Stationery Office, 1989.

3   Robinson R, Le Grand J. *Evaluating the NHS Reforms*. London: King's Fund, 1994.

4   Department of Health. *The NHS Plan: A plan for investment*. A plan for reform. London: The Stationery Office, 2000.

5   Speech to the Social Market Foundation, 20.03.02.

6   Asked by Tony McWalter if he would give 'a brief characterisation of the political philosophy that he espouses and which underlies his policies', the Prime Minister replied: 'The best example I can give is the rebuilding of the National Health Service today under this Government – extra investment...' *Hansard* 27.02.02, column 698, Prime Minister's Questions.

Chapter 2 – Funding

1   Appleby J. *Financing Health Care in the 1990s*. Milton Keynes: Open University Press, 1992.

2   HM Treasury. Spending Review 2000: *Prudent for a purpose: building opportunity and security for all*. London: The Stationery Office, 2000.

3   Mulligan J, Appleby J. The NHS and Labour's battle for public opinion. In: Park A *et al*. *British Social Attitudes: Public policy, social ties*. Eighteenth Report. London: Sage, 2001.

4   Blundell R, Reed H, Stoker T. *Interpreting aggregate wage growth*. Working Paper 99/13. London: Institute of Fiscal Studies, 1999.

5   Labour Party Manifesto. *New Labour: because Britain deserves better*. London: Labour Party, 1997.

6   Wanless, D. *Interim Report: Securing our Future Health: Taking a long-term view*. London: HM Treasury, 2001.

7   Appleby J. Spending under Labour. *Databriefing*. *Health Service Journal* 2001; 111; 5773: 29.

8   Treasury Select Committee. Eighth Report. *The New Fiscal Framework and the Comprehensive Spending Review*. Session 1997/98. London: House of Commons, 1998.

9   Appleby J, Boyle S. Blair's Billions: Where will he find the money? *British Medical Journal* 2000; 320: 865–7.

10 Towse A, Sussex J. Getting UK health care expenditure up to the European Union mean: what does that mean? *British Medical Journal* 2000; 320: 640–642.

11 Emmerson C, Frayne C and Goodman A. How much would it cost to increase UK health spending to the European Union average? *Briefing Note 21*. London: Institute for Fiscal Studies, 2002.

12 Appleby J, Boyle S. NHS spending: the wrong target (again)? In: Appleby J and Harrison A, editors. *Health Care UK: Spring 2001*, King's Fund.

13 Treasury Select Committee. Uncorrected Evidence. London: House of Commons, 2002. http://www.publications.parliament.uk/pa/cm200102/cmselect/cmtreasy/430/uc43001.htm

14 Wanless, D. *op.cit*.

15 Appleby J, Deeming C, Harrison A. The NHS: where has all the new money gone?. In: Appleby and Harrison, editors. *Health Care UK: Winter 2001*, King's Fund.

16 Mulligan, J, Appleby J, *op. cit.*
17 Appleby J, Boyle S, *op. cit.*

Chapter 3 – Waiting

1 Royal Commission on the NHS. Cmd 7615. London: The Stationery Office, 1979.
2 *The Patients' Charter: Raising the standard.* London: Department of Health, 1991.
3 Labour Party Manifesto. *New Labour: because Britain deserves better.* London: The Labour Party, 1997.
4 Department of Health. *The New NHS: Modern, dependable.* London: The Stationery Office, 1997.
5 Department of Health. *The NHS Plan: A plan for investment. A plan for reform*, London: The Stationery Office, 2000: Cmd 4818–I.
6 Department of Health. *The NHS Cancer Plan.* London: The Stationery Office, 2000.
7 National Audit Commission. *Inpatient and Outpatient Waiting in the NHS.* Report by the Comptroller and Auditor General. HC 221, Session 2001–2002. London: The Stationery Office, 2002.
8 *Ibid.*
9 Hospital Waiting Lists: April 2001. Health Statistics and Analysis Unit, NHS Wales. Press release (SDR 24/2001).
10 Modernisation Action Board. *Annual Report: The NHS Plan – a progress report.* London: NHS Executive, 2001.
11 *Review of National Findings: Accident and emergency.* Acute hospital portfolio No. 2. London: Audit Commission, 2001.
12 National Audit Commission. *Inappropriate adjustments to NHS waiting lists.* Report by the Comptroller and Auditor General. HC 452, Session 2001–2002. London: The Stationery Office, 2002.
13 Culyer AJ, Cullis JG. Some Economics of Hospital Waiting Lists in the NHS. *Journal of Social Policy* 1976; 5, 3, 239–64.
14 Luckman J, Mackenzie M, Stringer JC. *Management Policies for Large Ward Units.* Institute of Operational Research Health Report No. 1, 1969.
15 Baderman H *et al. Admission of Patients to Hospital.* London: King Edward's Hospital Fund, 1973.
16 Devlin N, Harrison A, Derrett S. Waiting in the NHS: Part 2: A change of prescription. *Journal of the Royal Society of Medicine,* 2002 (forthcoming).

Chapter 4 – Rationing

1 Hunter DJ. *Rationing dilemmas in health care.* NAHAT Research Paper No.8. Birmingham: National Association of Health Authorities and trusts, 1993.
2 Malone N, Rycroft-Malone J. Equity and rationing in the NHS: past to present. *Journal of Nursing Management* 1998; 6: 325–332.
3 Hunter, *op. cit.*
4 New B, Le Grand J. *Rationing in the NHS: Principles and pragmatism.* London: King's Fund, 1996.
5 New B. The rationing agenda in the NHS. In: New B, editor. *Rationing: talk and action.* London: King's Fund, 1997: Chapter 2.
6 Davies P. A conciliator putting his anxieties behind him. *Health Service Journal,* 28.02.91; p.15.
7 Doyal L. Rationing within the NHS should be explicit: the case for. In: New B, editor. *Rationing: talk and action.* London: King's Fund, 1997: Chapter 10.
8 Ham C, Coulter A. Introduction: international experience or rationing (or priority-setting). In: Coulter C, Ham C, editors. *The Global Challenge of Health Care Rationing.* Buckingham: Open University Press, Chapter 1.
9 *Ibid.*

10 New B, 1997, *op.cit.*

11 Labour Party Manifesto. *New Labour: because Britain deserves better*. London: The Labour Party, 1997.

12 Department of Health: *The NHS Plan: A plan for investment. A plan for reform*. London: The Stationery Office, 2000, Cmd 4818–I.

13 Labour Party Manifesto. *Ambitions for Britain*. London: The Labour Party, 2001.

14 Department of Health. *The New NHS: Modern, dependable*. London: The Stationery Office, 1997.

15 Labour Party 2001, *op.cit.*

16 Department of Health. *Faster Access to Modern Treatment: How NICE will work*. London: The Stationery Office, 1999.

17 Dewar S. Viagra: the political management of rationing. *Health Care UK* 1999/2000; 139–151.

18 Klein R, Williams A. Setting priorities: what is holding us back – inadequate information or inadequate institutions? In: Coulter C, Ham C, editors. *The Global Challenge of Health Care Rationing*. Buckingham: Open University Press, Chapter 2.

19 Raftery J. NICE: faster access to modern treatments? Analysis of guidance on health technologies. *British Medical Journal* 2001; 323:1300–1303.

20 http://www.nice.org.uk/article.asp?a=20860

21 Raftery J, *op.cit.*

22 Raftery J, *op.cit.*

23 Towse A. Does NICE have a threshold? An external view. In: Devlin N, Towse A, editors. *Cost-effectiveness Thresholds: Economic and ethical issues*. London: King's Fund/Office for Health Economics, 2002.

24 Devlin N, Parkin D, Appleby J. *Patients' Views of Explicit Priority Setting: What are the implications for NICE?* Unpublished paper, London: King's Fund, 2002.

25 http://www.doh.gov.uk/about/nhsplan/priorities/index.html

Chapter 5 – Primary care

1 NHS Executive. *Developing NHS Purchasing and GP Fundholding: towards a primary care-led NHS*. (EL(94)79) London: The Stationery Office, 1994.

2 Audit Commission. *What the Doctor Ordered: A study of GP fundholding in England and Wales*. London: The Stationery Office, 1996.

3 Le Grand J, Mays N, Mulligan J, editors. *Learning from the NHS Internal Market: A review of the evidence*. London: King's Fund, 1998.

4 Lewis R, Gillam S, editors. *Transforming Primary Care. Personal medical services in the new NHS*. London: King's Fund, 1999.

5 Secretary of State of Health. *Choice and Opportunity. Primary Care: The future*. London: The Stationery Office, 1996.

6 Department of Health. *The NHS (Primary Care) Act 1997*. London: The Stationery Office, 1997.

7 Labour Party Manifesto. *New Labour: because Britain deserves better*. London: The Labour Party, 1997.

8 Department of Health. *The New NHS: Modern, dependable*. London: The Stationery Office, 1997.

9 Calman K. *Developing Emergency Services in the Community. The final report*. London: NHS Executive, 1997.

10 Rosen R, Florin D. Evaluating NHS Direct. *British Medical Journal* 1999; 319: 5–6.

11 Department of Health. *The NHS Plan: A plan for investment. A plan for reform*. London: The Stationery Office, 2000, Cm 4818-I.

12 Department of Health. *Shifting the Balance of Power within the NHS: Securing delivery*. London: The Stationery Office, 2001.

13 *The New NHS: Modern and dependable: primary care groups: delivering the agenda*. HSC 1998/228. Leeds: Department of Health, 1998.

14 Smith J, Regen E, Goodwin N *et al. Getting Into Their Stride. Interim report of a national evaluation of primary care groups.* Birmingham: University of Birmingham, Health Services Management Centre, 2000.

15 Wilkin D, Gillam S, Coleman A, editors. *The National Tracker Survey of Primary Care Groups and Trusts: Modernising the NHS. 2000/2001.* London: National Primary Care Research and Development Centre/King's Fund, 2001.

16 The National PMS Evaluation Team. *National Evaluation of First Wave NHS Personal Medical Services Pilots: Integrated interim report from four research projects.* Manchester: National Primary Care Research and Development Centre, 2000.

17 Steiner A, editor. *Does PMS Improve Quality of Care?* Final Report from the Quality of Care Project, National Evaluation of PMS. NPCRDC/University of Southampton, November 2001.

18 Department of Health. *A First Class Service: Quality in the new NHS.* London: The Stationery Office, 1998.

19 Hayward J, Rosen R, Dewar S. Thin on the ground. *Health Services Journal* 1999; 26.08.99: 6–27.

20 Department of Health. *Supporting Doctors, Protecting Patients.* London: The Stationery Office, 1999.

21 Wye L, Rosen R, Dewar S. *Clinical Governance in Primary Care: A review of baseline assessments.* London: King's Fund, 2000.

22 Munro J, Nicholl J, O'Cathain A, Knowles E. *Evaluation of NHS Direct First Wave Sites. Second interim report to the Department of Health.* Sheffield: Medical Care Research Unit, University of Sheffield, 2000.

23 Mountford L, Rosen R. *NHS Walk-in Centres in London.* London: King's Fund, 2001.

24 Salisbury C, Chalder M, Manku Scott T, Pope C, Moore, L. The role of walk-in centres in the NHS. *British Medical Journal* 2002; 324: 399–402.

25 Lewis R, Gillam S. The NHS Plan – further reform of the British health service. *International Journal of Health Services* 2001; 31: 111–18.

26 Tobin T. Called to account. *Health Services Journal* 2002; 17.01.02: 22–24.

27 Gillam S. Homeward bound? Just how far have we come in re-directing resources to primary care? *Health Management* 2000; November: 14–15.

28 Gillam S, Abbott S, Banks-Smith J. Can primary care groups and trusts improve the population's health? *British Medical Journal* 2001; 323: 89–92.

29 Skrabanek P. *The Death of Humane Medicine and the Rise of Coercive Healthism.* London: Social Affairs Unit, 1994.

30 Fitzpatrick M. *The Tyranny of Health – Doctors and the regulation of lifestyle.* London: Routledge, 2001.

Chapter 6 – Workforce

1 Davies C. *Gender and the Professional Predicament in Nursing.* Buckingham: Open University Press, 1995.

2 Beardshaw V, Robinson R. *New for Old? Prospects for nursing in the 1990s.* London: King's Fund Institute, 1990.

3 Finlayson B. The recruitment and retention challenge. *Health Care UK*: Winter 2001; 42–50.

4 UKCC. *Annual statistics. Volume 1.* London: UKCC, 2000.

5 *Making Up the Difference: A review of the UK nursing labour market in 2000.* London: Royal College of Nursing, 2000.

6 Department of Health. *The New NHS: Modern, dependable.* London: The Stationery Office, 1997.

7 Department of Health. *Working Together: Securing a quality workforce for the NHS.* London: The Stationery Office, 1998.

8 Meadows S, Levenson R, Baeza J. *The Last Straw: Explaining the NHS nursing shortage*. London: King's Fund, 2000.

9 Department of Health. *Agenda for Change: Modernising the NHS Pay System*. London: The Stationery Office, 1999.

10 Department of Health. *The NHS Plan: A plan for investment. A plan for reform*. London: The Stationery Office, 2000.

11 NHS Executive. *Improving Working Lives in the NHS*. Department of Health. Health Service Circular, 1999/218.

12 Department of Health. *Making a Difference: Strengthening the nursing, midwifery and health visiting contribution to health and healthcare*. London: The Stationery Office, 1999.

13 House of Commons Health Select Committee. *Future NHS Staffing requirements*. Volume 1. London: The Stationery Office, 1999.

14 Department of Health. *Future Staffing Requirements: The Government's response to the health committee's report on future staffing requirements*. London: The Stationery Office, 1999.

15 Department of Health: *A Health Service of all the Talents: Developing the NHS workforce*. London: The Stationery Office, 2000.

16 *Ibid*; page 9.

17 Department of Health. *The NHS Plan, op.cit.*

18 Budget investment to target more GPs and nurses. Department of Health. Press release, 13.03.01.

19 Nurses, teachers and police officers get Government help to buy homes in housing hotspots. Department for Transport, Local Government and the Regions. Press release, 6.09.01.

20 Department of Health. *Improving Working Lives Standard: NHS employers committed to improving the working lives of people who work in the NHS*. London: The Stationery Office, 2000.

21 RCN response to new fund to address nurse recruitment and retention. Royal College of Nursing. Press release, 13.03.01.

22 General Practitioners Committee. *GPC News* 20.07.01.

23 Finlayson B, *op.cit.*

24 Smith G, Seccombe I. *Changing Times: A survey of registered nurses in 1998*. Brighton: Institute for Employment Studies, 1998.

25 Finlayson B. *Counting Smiles on Faces*. London: King's Fund, 2002.

26 Finlayson B, Dixon J, Meadows S, Blair G. In *Short Supply: The policy response to the shortage of NHS nurses*. Unpublished article, Sept 2001.

27 Wilkin D, Gillam S, Coleman A, editors. *The National Tracker Survey of Primary Care Groups and Trusts: Modernising the NHS. 2000/2001*. London: National Primary Care Research and Development Centre/King's Fund, 2001.

28 Wilson C. Extra posts set to push consultant expansion. *Hospital Doctor* 03.08.00.

29 *Position statement on the general practitioner workforce: one of a series of documents in response to the NHS Plan*. London: Royal College of General Practitioners, 2000.

30 *More NHS nurses, more NHS beds*. Department of Health. Press release, 12.12.01.

31 Meadows S, Levenson R, Baeza J. *The Last Straw: Explaining the NHS nursing shortage*. London: King's Fund, 2000.

32 Department of Health. *Vacancies Survey, March 2001*. London: The Stationery Office, 2001.

33 *Making Up the Difference: A review of the UK nursing labour market in 2000. Ibid*.

34 *Ibid*.

35 Department of Health. Statistical press notice, 5.02.02.

36 Taylor D, Esmail A. Retrospective analysis of census data on general practitioners who qualified in South Asia: who will replace them as they retire? *British Medical Journal* 1999; 318: 306–10.

37 Finlayson B. The recruitment and retention challenge, *op.cit.*

38 www.ucas.co.uk

39 Finlayson B. The recruitment and retention challenge, *op.cit.*

40 Department of Health. Statistical press notice, *op.cit.*

41 Department of Health. *Vacancies Survey, March 2001, op.cit.*

42 Audit Commission. *Review of national findings: Accident and Emergency.* London: Audit Commission, 2001.

43 Manley K, Garbett R. Paying Peter and Paul: Reconciling concepts of expertise with competency for a clinical career structure. *Journal of Clinical Nursing* 2000; 9,347–359.

44 Cochrane D, Conroy M, Crilly T, Rogers J. *The Future Healthcare Workforce: The second report.* Bournemouth: The University of Bournemouth, 1999.

45 Buchan J, Dal Poz M. *Role Definition, Skill Mix, Multi-Skilling and 'New' Workers.* http://www.who.int

Chapter 7 – Quality assurance

1 Kerrison S, Packwood T, Buxton M. Monitoring Medical Audit. In: Robinson R and Le Grand J, editors. *Evaluating the NHS Reforms.* London: King's Fund Institute, 1994.

2 The New Health Authorities and the Clinical Audit Initiative: outline of Planned Monitoring Arrangements. Department of Health, 1995 (Executive Letter: EL(95)103).

3 Improving Clinical Effectiveness. Department of Health, 1993 (Executive Letter: EL(93)115).

4 Improving the Effectiveness of the NHS. Department of Health, 1994 (Executive Letter: EL(94)74)

5 Improving the Effectiveness of Clinical Services. Department of Health, 1995 (Executive Letter: EL(95)105).

6 Humphris, D. *The Assisting Clinical Effectiveness (ACE) Programme.* ACE 1 Final Report Health Care Evaluation Unit. London: St George's Hospital Medical School, 1998.

7 Wye, L McClenahan, J. *Getting better with evidence: experiences of putting evidence into practice.* London: Kings Fund, 2000.

8 Evans D, Haines, A, editors. *Implementing Evidence-Based Changes in Healthcare.* Oxford: Radcliffe Medical Press, 2000.

9 Dunning, M. *Building on the Evidence: Learning from experience and evidence in everyday practice: the final report from the PACE programme.* London: King's Fund, 1999.

10 NHS centre for reviews and dissemination. Getting Evidence into practice. *Effective Health Care*, 5(1) 1999.

11 Department of Health. *Promoting Clinical Effectiveness – A framework for action in and through the NHS.* London: The Stationery Office, 1996.

12 Department of Health. *The New NHS: Modern, dependable.* London: The Stationery Office, 1997.

13 Bristol Royal Infirmary Public Inquiry. Public Inquiry into Children's Heart Surgery at the Bristol Royal Infirmary 1984–1995. In: *Learning from Bristol.* London: The Stationery Office, 2001 (Cmnd 5207).

14 Department of Health. *An Inquiry into Quality and Practice within the NHS Arising from the Actions of Rodney Ledward: The report.* London: The Stationery Office, 2000.

15 Royal Liverpool Children's Inquiry. *Royal Liverpool Children's Inquiry: report.* London: The Stationery Office, 2001.

16 Alan Milburn statement to the House of Commons: independent inquiry into issues raised by case of Dr Harold Shipman. Department of Health. Press release (2000/50) 27.01.00.

17 Department of Health. *Modernising Regulation in the Health Professions: Consultation Document.* London: The Stationery Office, 2001.

18 Department of Health. *Regulating Private and Voluntary Healthcare: Developing The Way Forward.* London: The Stationery Office, 2000.

19 Department of Health. *The Removal, Retention and use of Human Organs and Tissue from Post-mortem Examination*: Advice from the Chief Medical Officer. London: The Stationery Office, 2001.

20 Department of Health. *The New NHS: Modern, dependable, op. cit.*

21 Department of Health. *A First Class Service: Quality in the new NHS.* London: The Stationery Office, 1998.

22 Department of Health. *Supporting Doctors, Protecting Patients: A consultation paper on preventing, recognising and dealing with poor clinical performance of doctors in the NHS in England.* London: The Stationery Office, 1999.

23 John Denham Launches National Primary Care Development Team a major initiative to enable primary care to cut unnecessary deaths, improve patient access and tackle waiting lists and times. Department of Health. Press release, 02.02.00.

24 All hospitals to become star performers. Department of Health. Press release, 11.02.02.

25 Frank Dobson welcomes new NHS modernisation measures – new 'Modernisation Fund' for the NHS. Department of Health. Press release (98/272), 02.07.98.

26 New team to support NHS quality improvement. Department of Health. Press release, 11.08.99.

27 Modernisation Agency. *Service Improvement – Action on cancer, critical care, coronary heat disease. See* www.modern.nhs.uk

28 Department of Health. *The NHS Plan: A plan for investment. A plan for reform.* London: The Stationary Office, 2000.

29 Department of Health. *An Organisation with a memory – Report of an expert group on learning from adverse events in the NHS.* London: The Stationery Office, 2000.

30 Department of Health. *The New NHS: Modern and Dependable: A National Framework for Assessing Performance: Consultation Document.* London: The Stationery Office, 1998.

31 Department of Health. *Quality in the New NHS: High level performance indicators and clinical indicators.* London: The Stationery Office, 1999.

32 Department of Health. *Quality and Performance in the NHS: Performance indicators: July 2000.* London: The Stationery Office, 2000.

33 Department of Health. *National Service Framework for Mental Health.* London: The Stationery Office, 1999.

34 Department of Health. *National Service Framework for Coronary Heart Disease.* London: The Stationery Office, 2000.

35 Department of Health. *The NHS Cancer Plan: A plan for investment. A plan for reform.* London: The Stationery Office, 2000.

36 Department of Health. *A Policy Framework for Commissioning Cancer Services.* London: The Stationery Office, 1995.

37 Department of Health. *Diabetes: National Service Framework: Standards.* London: Department of Health, 2001.

38 Department of Health. *National Service Frameworks. See* www.doh.gov.uk/nsf

39 Department of Health. *A First Class Service – Quality in the new NHS, op.cit.*

40 Department of Health. Health Act 1999. London: The Stationery Office 1999.

41 Department of Health. *Primary Care Trusts – Establishing Better Services.* London: Department of Health, 2000.

42 The Commission for Health Improvement. See www.chi.nhs.uk

43 Department of Health. *The National Care Standards Act 2000.* London: The Stationery Office, 2000.

44 Department of Health. *The Care Homes Regulations 2001*: Statutory Instrument 2001 No 3965. London: The Stationery Office, 2001.

45 Department of Health. *Children's Homes Regulations 2001*: Statutory Instrument 2001 No 3967. London: The Stationery Office, 2001.

46 Department of Health. Private and Voluntary Health Care (England) Regulations 2001 No 3968. London: The Stationery Office, 2001.

47 Department of Health. *The NHS Plan – Implementing the Performance Improvement Agenda: A Policy Position Statement and Consultation Document.* London: The Stationery Office, 2000.

48 Department of Health. *NHS Performance Ratings: Acute Trusts 2000/01.* London: The Stationery Office, 2001.

49 Milburn A. Redefining the National Health Service. Speech given to New Health Network. 15.01.02.

50 All hospitals to become star performers. Department of Health. Press release, 11.02.02.

51 Department of Health. *The NHS Plan, op. cit.*

52 Department of Health. *Building a Safer NHS for Patients.* London: The Stationery Office, 2001.

53 *Protecting Patients: A summary consultative document.* London: General Medical Council, 2001.

54 Department of Health. *The NHS Plan, op. cit.*

55 Department of Health. *The National Care Standards Act 2000, op. cit.*

56 Department of Health. *Modernising Regulation: Establishing the new Nursing and Midwifery Council: a consultation document.* London: The Stationery Office, 2000.

57 Department of Health. *Modernising regulation: the new Health Professions Council: A consultation document.* London: The Stationery Office, 2000.

58 Department of Health. *Modernising Regulation in the Health Professions: consultation document.* London: The Stationery Office, 2001.

59 Department of Health. *Assuring the Quality of Medical Practice: Implementing supporting doctors protecting patients.* London: The Stationery Office, 2001.

60 *Interim protocol for contacts between the GMC and the NCAA.* General Medical Council, 2001.

61 *National Service Framework Assessments No.1: NHS Cancer Care in England and Wales.* Commission for Health Improvement and Audit Commission, 2001.

62 Sweeney G, Sweeny K, Greco M, Stead J. *Developing Clinical Governance in Primary Care: Briefing Paper 2:* Exploring the implementation and development of clinical governance within primary care in the South West. University of Exeter and Exeter and North Devon NHS Research and Development Support Unit, 2002.

63 Sweeney G, Sweeny K, Greco M, Stead J. *Developing Clinical Governance in Primary Care: Briefing Paper 1:* The experience of primary care clinical governance leads. University of Exeter and Exeter and North Devon NHS Research and Development Support Unit, 2002.

64 Department of Health. *Clinical Governance in London Trusts: Taking Stock: The 1999 London Regional stocktake of clinical governance: An overview of activities across all London trusts.* London: NHS London Regional Office, 2000.

65 Walshe K, Freeman T, Latham L, Wallace L, Spurgeon P. *Clinical Governance: From policy to practice*. University of Birmingham: Health Services Management Centre, 2000.

66 All hospitals to become star performers. Department of Health. Press release, 11.02.02.

67 Department of Health. *The NHS Plan – A Progress Report: The NHS Modernisation Board's Annual Report 2000–2001*. London: Department of Health, 2002.

68 *Ibid*.

69 *Ibid*.

70 *Review of Structure, Constitution and Governance*: Council, July 2001. General Medical Council (www.gmc-uk.org), 2001.

71 *Review of Fitness to practise: recommendations*: Council 5-6th November 2001 (item 10a). General Medical Council (www.gmc-uk.org), 2001.

72 General Medical Council. Revalidation: How will revalidation work. General Medical Council (www.gmc-uk.org/revalidation/revalfrm.html), 2001.

73 Bristol Royal Infirmary Public Inquiry. *Op.cit.*

Chapter 8 – The private sector

1 Department of Health. *The New NHS*. London: The Stationery Office, 1997.

2 Milburn A. *Redefining the National Health Service*. Speech to the New Health Network, 15.01.02.

3 *NHS Estate Management and Property Maintenance*. London: Audit Commission, 1991.

4 See, for example, Department of Health, National Audit Office. *Cost over-runs, funding problems and delays on Guy's Hospital Phase III development: report by the Comptroller and Auditor General*. London: National Audit Office, 1998.

5 Further details can be found in: Department of Health. *Departmental Report*. London: The Stationery Office, 2001.

6 Department of Health, The *NHS Plan: A plan for investment. A plan for reform*. London: The Stationery Office, 2000, para 11.6.

7 Department of Health and the Independent Healthcare Association. *For the Benefit of Patients: A concordat with the private and voluntary health care provider sector*. London: The Stationery Office, 2000.

8 Department of Health. *Building Capacity and Partnership in Care*. London: The Stationery Office, 2001.

9 The evidence on this is cited in Boyle S, Harrison A. The PFI in health: the story so far. In: Kelly G, Robinson P, editors. *A Healthy Partnership: The future of public–private partnerships in the health service*. London: Institute of Public Policy Research, 2000.

10 See the evidence of the Royal Berks and Battle Trust to the Health Select Committee Inquiry into the role of the private sector in the NHS: the committee report is due to be published later in 2002.

11 See, for example, *The PFI Report* December/January 2002, which states that some £4 billion of NHS deals were being held up. Guidance designed to speed up the negotiating process is to be published by the Office of Government Commerce later in 2002.

12 See, for example, Boyle S, Harrison A *op. cit.* and Sussex J. *The economics of the private finance initiative in the NHS*. London: Office of Health Economics, 2001. Also Gaffney D, Pollock A, Price D, Shaoul J. PFI in the NHS: is there an economic case? *British Medical Journal* 1999; 319: 249–253.

13 The Department of Health (like other central government) is required to publish a capital strategy. When the Department's first strategy appeared in 1999 (*Capital Investment Strategy for the Department of Health*. Leeds: Department of Health), it simply ignored what was happening to hospital buildings.

14 Department of Health. *Shaping the Future NHS*. London: The Stationery Office, 2000.

15 Ferguson, M. *Progress through Partnership*. London: The Stationery Office, 1995.

16 These are brought out in Francis S, Glanville R. *Building a 2020 Vision: Future health care environments*. London: The Stationery Office, 2001.

17 *NHS and BUPA negotiate new public private relationship*. Department of Health Press release, 2001/0593. The intention is for the NHS to take over use of the hospital but for BUPA to continue to manage it under contract.

18 Coates P. Don't shoot the messenger. *Public Finance*. 25.08.00.

19 *Financial Times* 19.01.02, p.2.

20 This issue was raised 20 years ago in McLachlan G, Maynard A, editors. *The Public/Private Mix for Health*. The Nuffield Provincial Hospitals Trust, 2002. Alan Maynard pointed out that other sectors are now expected to pay for the training of those they employ. However, if purchasers were to be able to choose between private and public suppliers, then training costs would need to be paid for in a way that did not distort the choice between them.

21 Speech to New Health Network 15.01.02.

22 Timmins N, *Financial Times* 19.01. 02.

23 Timmins N, *Financial Times* 21.01.02.

24 Department of Health. *Working for Patients*.London: The Stationery Office, 1989.

25 *The Times,* 6.02.01, p. 1.

Chapter 9 – Long-term care

1 Department of Health. *A New Partnership for Care in Old Age*. London: The Stationery Office, 1996.

2 Department of Health. *NHS and Community Care*. London: The Stationery Office, 1990.

3 Department of Health. Community Care – September SSI / RHA Monitoring. EL (93) 119; CI (93) 35; Department of Health. Community Care Monitoring for 1994/5. EL (94) 57; CI (94) 57; Department of Health. NHS responsibilities for meeting continuing health care needs. HSG (95) 8; LAC (95) 5.

4 Winter cash boost for priority services. Department of Health. Press release 24.12.96.

5 UK Home Care Association. *Response to 'Moving Forward' and the Burgner Report*. Sowerby Bridge: UK Home Care Association, 1996.

6 Labour Party Manifesto. *New Labour: because Britain deserves better*. London: The Labour Party, 1997.

7 Frank Dobson issues NHS guidance on winter planning. Department of Health. Press release, 29.08.97.

8 Frank Dobson announces distribution of extra cash for the NHS this year. Department of Health. Press release, 22.10.97.

9 Labour Party Manifesto. *Ambitions for Britain*. London: The Labour Party, 2001.

10 Department of Health. *The NHS Plan: A plan for investment. A plan for reform*. London: The Stationery Office, 2000.

11 Royal Commission on Long-term Care. *With Respect to Old Age: Long-term care – rights and responsibilities*. London: The Stationery Office, 1999.

12 Health Secretary announces setting up of national care commission. Department of Health. Press release, 02.12.99.

13 Secretary of State for Health. *The NHS Plan – the Government's response to the Royal Commission on Long-term Care*. London: The Stationery Office, 2000.

14 Fairer home care charges to benefit thousands. Department of Health. Press release, 23.11.01.

15 Poxton, R. *Partnerships in Primary and Social Care – integrating services for vulnerable people*. London: King's Fund, 1999.

16 Department of Health. *The Health and Social Care Act*. London: The Stationery Office, 2001.

17 Department of Health. *Domiciliary Care – National Minimum Standards Regulations Consultation Document*. London: The Stationery Office, 2001.

18 New national standards and regulations for care homes issued. Department of Health. Press release, 13.12.01.

19 Department of Health. *National Service Framework on Mental Health*. London: The Stationery Office, 1999.

20 Department of Health *National Service Framework on Older People*. London: The Stationery Office, 2001.

21 Help the Aged Policy Statement: Long-term Care, London: Help the Aged, September 2001.

22 Response to the Government's announcement on long-term care for older people and the NHS Plan. Age Concern England, 27.07.00.

23 British Medical Association. Doctors decry a tax on the sick. Press release, 5.02.01.

24 RCN Public Affairs Briefing: the funding of long-term care. July 2000.

25 Robinson, J. Reforming long-term care finances: a continuing saga. *Health Care UK: Winter 2000*. King's Fund.

26 Prime Minister's statement on the National Health Service Plan. 27.07.00.

27 *The Coming of Age: Improving care services for older people*. London: Audit Commission, 1997.

28 *Shaping the Future NHS: Long-term planning for hospitals and related services*. Consultation document on the findings of the National Beds Inquiry. London: Department of Health, 2000.

29 Department of Health. *The NHS Plan, op.cit.*

30 Department of Health *Building Capacity and Partnership in Care*. London: The Stationery Office, 2001.

31 Department of Health. *NHS Modernisation Board Annual Report*. London: The Stationery Office, 2002.

32 Milburn, A. Speech to the Annual Social Services Conference. 19.10.01.

33 *Meeting the Standards? Analysis of the First Round of Local 'Better Care, Higher Standards' charters*. Leeds: Nuffield Institute for Health, 2000.

34 Henwood, M. *Future Imperfect – Report of the King's Fund Care and Support Inquiry*. London: King's Fund, 2001.

35 *A New Contract for Retirement*. London: Institute for Public Policy and Research, Forthcoming 2002.

36 Banks, P. *Partnerships under Pressure – an interim report*. London: King's Fund, 2002.

Chapter 10 – Patient and public involvement

1 Griffiths, R. *The NHS Management Inquiry*, London: DHSS, 1983.

2 Department of Health. *Being Heard*: The Report of a Review Committee on NHS Complaints Procedures. London: The Stationery Office, 1994.

3 Department of Health. *Local Voices: The views of local people in purchasing for health*, London: The Stationery Office, 1992.

4 Milewa T *et al*. Managerialism and active citizenship in Britain's reformed health service. *Social Science and Medicine* 1998; 47 (4): 507–517).

5 Labour Party Manifesto. *New Labour: because Britain deserves better*. London: The Labour Party: 1997.

6 Hutton W. The State We're In. In: Hall S, Hall W, editors. *Ego Trip: Extra-governmental Organisations in the UK and their Accountability*, London: Vintage, 1996.

7 Department of Health. *The New NHS: Modern, dependable*. London: The Stationery Office, 1997.
Department of Health. *The NHS Plan: A plan for investment. A plan for reform*. London: The Stationery Office, 2000.

8 Labour Party Manifesto. *Ambitions for Britain*. London: The Labour Party, 2001.

9 More patients go ahead for treatment. Department of Health. Press release, 15.10.01.

10 Department of Health. NHS Performance Indicators (www.doh.gov.uk)

11 Department of Health. *Your Guide to the NHS*. London: The Stationery Office, 2001.

12 Department of Health. *Extending Patient Choice*. London: The Stationery Office, 2002.

13 Department of Health. *Reforming the Complaints Procedure: A listening document*. London: The Stationery Office, 2001.

14 O'Caithan O *et al*, How helpful is NHS Direct? Postal survey of callers. *British Medical Journal* 2000: 15.04.00. 320:1035

15 Munro J *et al*. *Evaluation of NHS Direct First Wave Sites: First interim report to the Department of Health, Medical Research Unit*. Sheffield: University of Sheffield, 1998.

16 Mountford L, Rosen R. *NHS Walk-in-Centres in London: An initial assessment*. London: King's Fund, 2001.

17 McInerney J *et al*. Impact of NHS Direct on intermediate care. *British Medical Journal* 28.10.00; 321: 1077.

18 Commissioner for Public Appointments, *Sixth Report, Office of the Commissioner for Public Appointments*, London: OPCA, 2001.

19 Commissioner for Public Appointments. *Public appointments to NHS Trusts and Health Authorities*, London: OPCA, March 2000.

20 Anderson W, Florin D. *Involving the Public – One of Many Priorities: A survey of public involvement in London's primary care groups*. London: King's Fund, 2000.

21 Anderson W, Florin D, Mountford L, Gillam S. *Every Voice Counts: Primary care organisations and public involvement*. London: King's Fund, 2002.

22 Department of Health. *Handling Complaints: Monitoring the NHS complaints procedures. England, financial year 2000/01*. London: The Stationery Office, 2001.

23 NHS Executive. *National Survey of NHS Patients: general practice*. London: NHS Executive, 1999.

24 Bell A. Dr Foster went to Coventry (and Bristol), *British Journal of Health Care Management* 2001; 7 (12): 403 (December 2001).

25 Department of Health. *Analysis of responses to the NHS Plan public consultation*. Accessed at www.doh.gov.uk/nhsplan/shiftinggearsanalysis.htm

26 Anderson W, Florin F. Consulting the public about the NHS, *British Medical Journal* 10.06.00; 320:1553–1554.

Chapter 11 – Health inequalities

1 Trends in life expectancy by social class 1972–1999, http://www.statistics.gov.uk/products/p8460.asp

2 Black D, Morris J, Smith C, Townsend P. *Inequalities in Health: Report of a Research Working Group*. London: Department of Health and Social Security, 1980.

3 *The Health of the Nation: A strategy for health in England*. London: The Stationery Office, July 1992.

4 *Independent inquiry into inequalities in health*: The Acheson report. London: The Stationery Office, 1998.

5 Department of Health. *Our Healthier Nation: A contract for health*. London: The Stationery Office, 1998.

6 Department of Health. *Saving lives: Our healthier nation*. London: The Stationery Office, 1999.

7 Department of Health, *Reducing Health Inequalities: An Action Report,* London, Department of Health, 1999.

8 http://www.labour.org.uk/

9 http://www.doh.gov.uk/himp/index.htm

10 http://www.haznet.org.uk/

11 The HAZ website, http://www.haznet.org.uk/

12 http://www.hmtreasury.gov.uk/spending_review/spending_review_2000/spending_review_report/spend_sr00_repchap23.cfm

13 Local Government Association, Facts about LSPs, London LGA, 2001.

14 *Op. cit.*

15 Bull J, Hamer L. *Closing the Gap: Setting local targets to reduce health inequalities.* London: Health Development Agency, 2001.

16 Department of Health. *The NHS Plan: A plan for investment. A plan for reform.* London: The Stationery Office, 2000.

17 Department of Health. *Tackling Health Inequalities: Consultation on a plan for delivery.* London: The Stationery Office, 2001.

18 Department of Health. *National Service Framework for Coronary Heart Disease.* London: The Stationery Office, 2001.

19 Department of Health. *The NHS Cancer Plan.* London: The Stationery Office, 2001.

20 http://www.doh.gov.uk/allocations/review/address.htm

21 Shaw R, Smith P. Allocating health care resources to reduce health inequalities. *Health Care UK: Spring 2001.* King's Fund.

22 Insalaco R. *Annual Abstract of Statistics.* London: Office for National Statistics, 2002.

23 *Family Resources Survey,* London: Office for National Statistics, 2001.

24 Carvel J. Tories scorn Brown over child poverty. The Guardian. 14.12.01.

25 *Youth Cohort Study.* London: Office for National Statistics, 2001.

26 *London: A healthy place to live? 2002 Update on the London Health Strategy high level indicators,* Table 3. London: London Health Commission, 2002.

27 Insalaco R, *op.cit.*

28 *Labour Force Survey.* London: Office for National Statistics, 2001.

29 *Living in Britain.* London: Office for National Statistics, 2000.

30 Rahman M, Palmer G, Kenway P. *Monitoring Poverty and Social Exclusion 2001.* York: Joseph Rowntree Foundation, 2001.

31 Department of Health. *Health Survey for England: Trend Data for Adults.* London: The Stationery Office, 1993–2000.

32 Fitzpatrick J, Jacobson B. *Mapping Health Inequalities Across London.* London: London Health Observatory, 2001. *See also* http://www.statistics.gov.uk/downloads/theme_health/HSQ12_v2.pdf

33 *Trends in life expectancy by social class 1972–1999.* London: Office for National Statistics, 2002.

34 *Mortality Statistics.* Series DH2 no.27. London: Office for National Statistics, 2000.

04695555